A Manual of

ANNI DIXON

A Manual of Healing

Ashgrove Press, Bath

First published in Great Britain by
ASHGROVE PRESS LIMITED
4 Brassmill Centre, Brassmill Lane
Bath BA1 3JN
and distributed in the USA by
Avery Publishing Group Inc.
120 Old Boradway
Garden City Park
New York 11040

ISBN 1-85398-024-2

First published 1992

Photoset in Palatino by
Ann Buchan Typesetters, Middlesex
Printed and bound in Great Britain by
Dotesios Ltd, Trowbridge, Wiltshire

CONTENTS

This book is dedicated to the people and the land of Eire, the Emerald Isle, where the Heart is radiant and alive.

A Manual of Healing

BEFORE WE BEGIN

The information given in this book is not expected to be of much help to complete beginners. Although there will be many things of interest to the beginner, the system of healing described is too subtle and yet potent for it to be of much use until some other system has first been mastered. The book is intended for people already using reflexology, shiatsu, aromatherapy, chiropractic, acupuncture or other manual therapy. It is hoped that what I offer you here will enable you to deepen the skills and knowledge you are already using.

If you have experience in one or more of these skills, you will already have developed a sensitivity in your hands and finger-tips to tension levels in the body and the different ways in which these levels manifest, and change, as they respond to treatment. This sensitivity is essential if you are to make use of the information contained in this book. Without it you have no sense of how to interpret what your fingertips experience as they release the points with which you are working. It would be extremely cumbersome to describe in a book the numerous ways in which tension manifests and responds. The method of healing described in these pages is an advanced one, only really suitable for people already experienced in some form of alternative therapy.

I know the book will raise as many questions as it answers – perhaps more! The subject is so fascinating and so profound that it would be impossible to cover in detail all the areas of interest that it touches upon. Such a book would contain more than our minds could cope with in one go. To me our world is seething with urgent and desperate need; my aim here has been to approach tending this need in the most practical terms possible. I don't think it is very practical usually to get involved in lengthy discussions about, for instance, reincarnation, or what colour each centre should carry. I want, if I possibly can, to help you to better understand your patient's problem, so you can more

11

effectively help him or her to get well now, immediately.

The system described in these pages may at first seem very complex; yet it is at root very simple. The first essential principles are few and there is an underlying pattern of simplicity which repeats itself continuously. Once these essential principles, and the pattern they reiterate, is grasped, the apparently diverse threads of the approach will emerge with coherence, and be easily applied. However, it is not possible to properly understand these without actually practising the approach and this is why it is really necessary to already have the experience of some other manual skill at your fingertips.

I suggest that you read the book the whole way through first, not trying to grapple much with the bits that don't immediately fit into place in your mind . . . trust that experience of the method, and frequent re-readings, will unfold the deeper understanding not always possible at first.

Having read the book quickly, begin to explore your relationship with the Soul. A book which will help this exploration is William Bloom's *Meditation in a Changing World* (1987, Gothic Image Publications, Glastonbury). Any previous experience of meditation or even contemplative prayer will help you to take the first steps towards identifying with your own Soul (cf. p. 174).

When you begin to feel that you have a sense of how to connect with your Soul, embark upon using the release patterns. This manual part of the healing approach is a particular technique called Jin Shin Do (The Way of the Compassionate Spirit). If you wish to know more about this technique, there is a textbook describing its history and practise: 'Acupressure Way of Health: Jin Shin Do' by Iona Teeguarden (Japan Publications, Inc., Tokyo, Japan, 1978.)

Between doing release patterns on family, friends or patients, refer back to the sections in this book which discuss the particular pattern you have been working on, and frequently re-read the section on the liver and kidneys, and that describing the way in which tensions accumulate, and how they are drained away by the healer.

And continue to work, in meditation, on your relationship with the Soul.

You will find, as you pursue this inner and outer work, that the principles at the heart of this healing system become clear and meaningful, and that your understanding of what you are doing, and why, deepens.

If it is possible, an excellent way to learn how to heal in this way would be to gather together with a group of others. The Soul relationship can be greatly developed and given perspective through working at its unfoldment in group formation; also you can practise the release patterns upon each other in an atmosphere of acceptance and mutual interest; and the discussions that follow both meditation and practise would rapidly enable your knowledge and understanding to grow. However, you should definitely still give time each day to affirming your personal relationship with the Soul and there are meditations given in this book which can be used for this and for group work (Group: Walking Meditation, p. 28; Meditation on the Radiation of Love, p. 67; Personal: Radiation of Love and Daily Meditation routine, p. 195).

Even though the book may seem full of lengthy theoretical sections, it is in fact extremely practical. All the words are intended to convey an understanding of the subtler workings of the human being, in its context of a greater universal system which I refer to as the Divine Life. To me, we as individuals are parts of an enormous integrated life which we are as yet too undeveloped to grasp, see or understand in its entirety. But this enormous life exists according to a pattern which is repeated throughout itself, and which is very simple. This pattern is based upon three types of force: active, receptive and relating. These are the three essential factors in all of life. They can be found to underly all forms at the microcosmic, the human and the macrocosmic levels. These three essential factors relate to each other in different ways throughout the spectrum of life, and the different relationships produce different expressions which distract and confuse us and make it difficult for us to see through the outward, diverse expressions, to the inner, consistent and harmonious theme, or principle.

The healing method described here seeks to interpret a patient's symptoms as expressions of his or her relationship with his outward and diversified self, and the inner essential self which is one with all other inner selves, and therefore also with the One Divine Life. In this sense the healing carried out is 'spiritual healing'. This is because it aims to allow wholeness and harmony to be achieved between the outward personality and the inward Soul or spiritual self.

Nevertheless it is a method which is extremely potent at adjusting physical problems; sometimes it is dramatically and miraculously effective in dealing with these. In the text I refer mostly to the adjustment of the emotional life of the patient. This is because it is primarily conflict and congestion in the emotional life which causes problems at the other levels of physical and mental bodies. Emotional and mental problems can also be caused by a physical problem; and emotional and physical problems can be brought on from the mental level; but mostly imbalances or dis-ease will originate from the emotional level and draining and clarifying this 'body' will be the main task.

The first aim with a patient will be to get a better relationship or flow of energy between his or her physical and emotional bodies; next the relationship between the emotional and the mental bodies will be adjusted; and lastly, if the patient seeks this, the relationship between these three 'bodies' and the spiritual 'body' will be adjusted.

It is the relationship between the four parts of the personality: the physical, emotional, mental and spiritual bodies which has become clogged and distorted and it is the 'joints' between these four parts which must be 're-conditioned'. We are able to influence these inter-relationships because the healing we are doing works directly upon the nervous system, and it is the nervous system which is the factor which integrates physical with emotional, emotional with mental, and these three with the spiritual self.

The nervous system itself works at different levels. It is best known as the nerves of the brain and spinal cord, carrying messages out to every part of the peripheral body, and then back again. It is a system for the transmission of information through the body. But it also functions at a subtler level. The brain is so constructed that it is able to receive electrical impulses, and to convert these into chemical instructions which are carried through the body. The brain responds to electrical impulses which are found at random on the wavelength of the mental plane, and it also can tune itself to respond to specific electrical impulses which its own wavelength is able readily to harmonise with. Wherever the impulse comes from, it evokes a chemical response in the body, as it is transmitted through the nervous system.

This principle causes some people to fall ill, but it also is what enables us to carry through healing of a very profound nature. The one who falls ill responds too easily to random impulses through his nervous system, whilst the healer is able to tune himself to the radiant inspiration and clarification of the wave-length of the Soul, and can then transmit this to the ill person, bringing about a re-tuning, in time, of his nervous system so that it is able to receive directly, the inflow of radiant clarity and vitality from the Soul.

In this context, the nervous system that we have described in our individual bodies, extends way out through the Soul and universe. This is exactly what is happening, and the technical term used to describe this extended nervous system is the etheric field. The etheric field is one; it is nowhere disconnected from elsewhere in itself. However, around individual entities it gathers into an intensity of concentration and we call this the etheric vehicle of a person. The etheric vehicle of each of us is affected by our physical, emotional, mental and spiritual experience. It can become very furred up, thick and congested if we are not careful to keep it clear and radiant. When it becomes congested or thickened, cloudy or dark, so also does our experience of our life.

The system of healing described in this book uses the etheric vehicle of the healer to cleanse and revitalise the etheric vehicle of the patient. In other words, we use our own nervous system to adjust the nervous system of our patient. This is why the relationship with the Soul is so important. Through holding our nervous systems tuned to the wavelength of the Soul, the energy of the Soul is able to be drawn through the etheric vehicle of the healer to the patient, where it can rapidly set to work to melt away obstructions and distortions.

There are three branches to this method of healing: the work of the hands, using Jin Shin Do, the work of the head, using the relationship with the Soul, and the third activity which relates the other two and produces a picture of the state of the patient's physical, emotional, mental and spiritual condition.

A The work of the hands

Jin Shin Do, or the Way of the Compassionate Spirit, uses thirty points (and some extra ones) drawn from the twelve major meridians of acupuncture. These points are used in patterns called the eight Strange Flows. These Strange Flows have a profound regulatory effect upon the major acupuncture meridians (for more information, please see Iona Teeguarden's book). In the method used in this book, we do not actually touch the body, except when we need to slide our hands under our patient in order to reach points on or near the spine.

Some healers will prefer to use the fingertips, others the palms of the hands. Whichever is used, it is not essential to locate the point used with the kind of anatomical accuracy necessary in either acupuncture or acupressure. Cover the area of the point with either the three middle fingertips, or the palm of the hand, affirm your alignment with the Soul, and wait without effort until you sense some energy response in your fingertips. It will always take a little time before this response comes. When it does, what you are experiencing is the draining of tension from that point in the etheric vehicle as it responds to the magnetic pull of your hands.

B The work of the head

We use our minds actively to assert our relationship with the Soul. This is absolutely essential to this way of healing. If it is ignored, you will still have some effect upon your patient, but it will lack the profound influence and understanding made possible through the relationship with the Soul. Also, it is possible that your exchange of energy with your patient will leave you adversely affected by your patient's state. 'Spiritual hygiene' is essential if we are not to lose our own integrity and identity in this work. It is the Soul which maintains this hygiene.

As healers we are only active in the sense that with determination we hold our personality quiescent and tuned to the Soul, so that the Soul may use us to distribute its own quality of energy more freely through people. The energy of the Soul is focussed through our minds, and grounded or anchored upon Earth through our hands as they work with people in distress.

C The work of relating

In time we become adept at sensing the state of energy flow or inhibition, at each point we work with; in time also, we learn, through our unfolding sense of what each point relates to, and the Key of the Centres, to relate the tension state of a point in one part of the body, with that of points elsewhere; we find, bit by bit, a pattern emerging that reveals to us which centres are most clogged, which most dynamically freeing of tension. We begin to recognise that the changes our patient is experiencing between sessions are directly linked with the areas most dramatically freeing at the previous session. And we begin to notice that tension release and healing change takes place in a cyclic fashion: first outer layers of tension are softened and loosened; then they are released, possibly accompanied by some difficult experience in the outer life of the patient; and then the etheric vehicle rests and gathers its strength to bring a shedding of a deeper and tighter layer of tension. . . Our alignment with the Soul casts insight into our minds which helps us to piece together the information of tension levels revealed to us by our hands.

I have already said that essentially this method of healing is simple. That is true because the essential principles are straight-forward, and reflected everywhere around and within us. How-ever, these essential principles give rise to innumerable and diverse expressions and combinations of expressions, all flowing in and out of each other in what seems to be a random fashion and yet does actually have purpose and intention.

If we remain open, we can be drawn into an experience of life at its simplest, at its essence (which is also its most intense!) and we can re-emerge from this into an experience of life at its most versatile and rich. I have tried (only you can tell me if I have succeeded!) to present this book in a way which will help you, its reader, to share this awareness of the essential simplicity and the peripheral complexity of life, with me . . . we can ride the wave of space and time up into its crest, where both dimensions merge and we taste the raw immediacy of our spirit, and slide down into its trough, where all things stretch out before us and we can savour and enjoy our bodies and the experience we can explore through them.

However, I cannot supply you with an open mind . . . this you must bring with you if you wish really to gain anything from our journey of exploration through this book. But no learning, no extension of ourselves, can take place without an open mind and I trust that anyone interested enough to buy a book such as the one I offer you here, is already endowed with such an essential life-tool.

I have arranged the book in such a way that you are introduced first to some of the theory at its most accessible. You are led from here into the practical release patterns themselves, and from here into the theory once more, but at a deeper level.

I have tried as much as possible to avoid terminology which needs a glossary to be deciphered. It seems to me that if indeed the three essential principles which form the key of life are reflected in and through all forms of life, these principles should be able to be discussed in language which is also reflected through all forms of life. This is not always easy to do, because those three principles, when described as an essence, are abstracted from any obvious or visible or tangible form; they are stripped of their outer clothing, and so we have to use words to describe them which are also abstracted from an outer clothing. I have done this only when really necessary, and tried the rest of the time to clothe the three principles of Spirit, Soul and Matter, with images which reveal rather than disguise, their essential nature.

I have written the book mostly in terms of a scientific interpretation: in terms of knowledge of what is. It would in many ways be easier for me to write in devotional and mystical terms. But religious doctrines have alienated our thought from the idea of God to an extraordinary extent. I seem always to be coming across people who come out in purple and orange spots as soon as I mention the word 'God'! Even people who are disciplined followers of meditation often cannot abide the thought of God. For others God is an accepted idea, but always held at a distance, untouchable and unreachable. Our efforts to understand our world in the scientific terms of knowledge have separated us from an easy ability to experience the presence of God.

For me, personally, life has no meaning unless I am experiencing the presence of God; it is a drab and hollow round of pleasure-seeking activities combined with desperate efforts to survive in a world of material competitiveness and confusion. For me healing is an experience of the presence of God. I experience my life with an intensity which is frequently uncomfortable and rarely communicable in terms which have meaning for others. Such sensitivity and intensity, whilst being wearying, also opens me constantly to a sense of the presence of God flowing in and through and around me and that gives my life tremendous richness and challenge. I feel raw and over-exposed frequently, yet also I can hear and touch and share the ecstasy of the Spirit as it unfolds its exuberant and joyous dance of exploration through my form . . . the time will come when my form, my personality, will no longer be able to respond or provide creative scope for the Spirit to adventure through . . . my personality will sink down to Earth like a leaf in the fall, but the spirit will leap up as always like the phoenix and continue its ecstatic and jubilant dance in and out through other forms. Whether we like, believe, or accept this principle or not, this is the way of life that we are subjected to: it happens anyway, regardless of our belief systems.

You don't need to accept or reject my devotional and mystical attitude in order to use this method of healing . . . this book is written as much as possible in neutral terms. If you can open your mind to the key suggested (active, receptive and relating frequencies of energy), and also to your own relationship with the Soul as the energy frequency which relates your personality to the energy frequency of the essential life-force, you can pursue this method of healing. If you can do these things, it will undoubtedly bring you an enriched understanding of life-forces, and a constant consequent deepening of the tapestry of your own personal experience.

I wish you the best of good luck on your journey. . . May God bless you and keep you from harm!

I am your friend, and my love for you goes deep.
There is nothing I can give you which you have not got;
But there is much, very much, that while I cannot give it,
You can take.
                    No heaven can come to us, unless our hearts
Find rest in today. Take Heaven!
No peace lies in the future which is not hidden
In this present little moment. Take Peace!
                    The gloom of the world, is but a shadow.
Behind it, yet within our reach, is joy.
There is radiance and glory in the darkness,
Could we but see, and to see we have only to look.
I beseech you to look.
                    Life is so generous a giver, but we
Judging its gifts by their covering,
Cast them away as ugly, or heavy, or hard.
Remove the covering and you will find beneath it
A living splendour, woven of love, by wisdom, with power.
                    Welcome it, touch it, and you will touch the
Angel's hand that brings it to you.
                    Everything we call a trial, a sorrow or a duty,
Believe me, that Angel's hand is there; the gift is there.
And the wonder of an overshadowing presence.
Our joys too: be not content with them as joys.
They too conceal diviner gifts.
                    Life is so full of meaning and purpose,
So full of beauty — beneath its covering —
That you will find earth but cloaks your heaven.
                    Courage then to take it: that is all!
But courage you have; and the knowledge that we
Are pilgrims together.
Wending through unknown country, home.
                    And so, at this time, I greet you.
Not quite as the world sends greetings,
But with profound esteem and with the prayer
That for you now and forever
The day breaks and the shadows flee away.

                                        Fra GIOVANNI 1513 AD

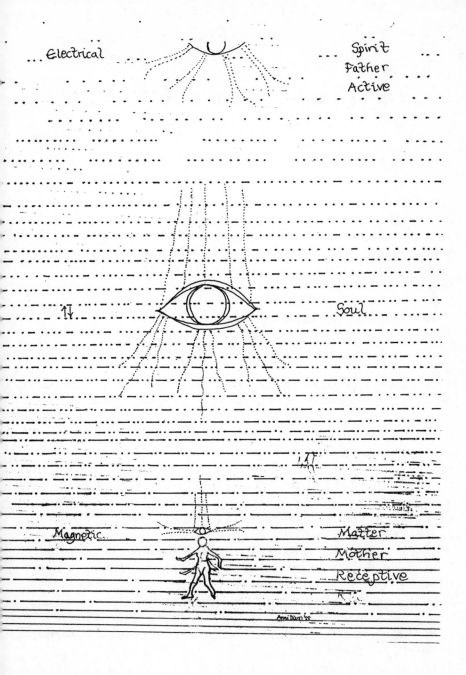

Figure 1

1. The Three-Cornered Key of Life:
First Principles

We exist in a system which is one everywhere . . . i.e. it is UNIVERSAL. However, the stage of development of our senses of perception do not allow us to experience this through our whole beings, but simply as a nice idea. We strive towards a state of such deep and thorough self-knowledge that we may experience this absolute Oneness, and therefore, no more need to strive. We approach this state through a gradual exploration and under-standing of our selfhood and of our environment.

Figure 1 seeks to illustrate the constitutional makeup of the universal being, and our place as a tiny individual part within that.

The universal plane of being is made up of continuously interacting frequencies of electrical and magnetic force. As the electrical is transformed into the magnetic and back again, its frequency, or rate of vibration, gradually changes from fast to slow, producing as it does so planes of specific frequency which can be distinguished from the whole.

Within this field of continuous electro-magnetic activity an organ is born, where that activity condenses or becomes particu-larly intense. The organ is the mind and the field within which it exists is its realm of activity. The organ – the mind – is active – it possesses intention; whereas the field it explores is receptive. Thus the organ, or mind, is most pure or concentrated, at the level of frequency of electricity and Spirit (cf. chart); whereas the field it explores is most pure and concentrated at the level of frequency of magnetism and Matter. The mind enables the field of the universe to know itself, through a steady exploration and experience of that field.

The universal mind implants itself in the limited prison of an individual body (belonging to Matter) and proceeds to achieve self knowledge from the level of that body. This mind has the innate capacity to transform the frequency of force transmission within the universal plane but it can only consciously achieve this by learning to tune itself to the frequency of the organ of mind at that level, or rate of vibration, more subtle than its own.

We use meditation to become attuned first, to the frequency of the Soul and then, having been absorbed into and adjusted by this, to the frequency of the Spiritual Triad.

The material or physical plane is the one we inhabit and our bodies are constructed of physical atoms originating from this material plane. But the material plane itself contains the remains of all physical life since the beginning of time, which includes un-measurable quantities of feelings and thoughts, mostly self-centred: feelings of greed, anger, jealousy, hatred, fear and thoughts of personal power or destructiveness towards others.

These thoughts and feelings have coloured and clung to the material realm, especially when the spirit-bodies of the people carrying those thoughts and feelings have not completely let go of their earthly attachments.

When we come to birth we are, to a greater or lesser extent, receptive to our environment, and so we absorb into ourselves much of the residues that cling to the places and people in that environment. This is added to the residues of unclear, subtle substance that we bring with us from previous lifetimes. This is the case for each and every one of us. So each of us is in a sense a victim of our personal past, but also of our shared, group past as members of the human race.

This subtle substance permeates our beings and if we are predominantly receptive people, with underactive livers and weak kidneys, we will continue to absorb the subtle dross around us and eventually fall ill. The inflow of lifeforce from the universal source of being weakens because it is blocked by the layers of congestion surrounding us. Our minds become tangled and confused and unable to reach up through the congestion to the clear plane of the Soul, and to bring inspiration and under-standing from that realm.

To reconnect ourselves with the universal source of our being we have to clear this congestion in the subtle or etheric body, or vehicle.

We are better able to do this if we know something about the constitution of each of us as individual human beings.

Congestion builds up in our subtle bodies because we are born into an extremely congested environment. The creative

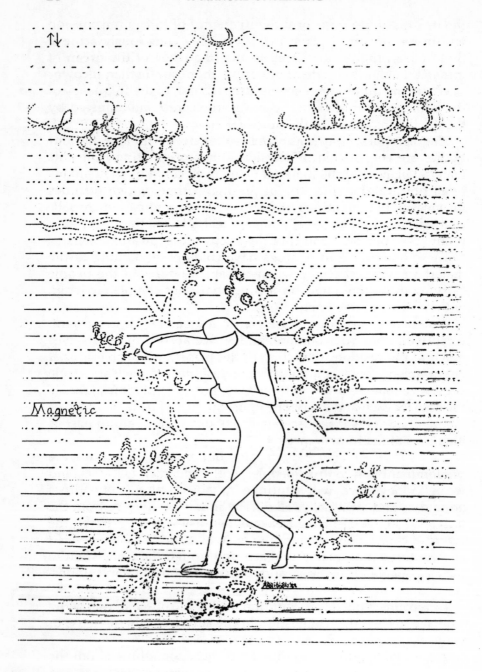

Figure 2

centres (THROAT and PELVIS) in the subtle body, the gateways, become locked and stuck. This results in a build-up of emotional force imprisoned in the chest and digestive areas. This can cause either a complete numbing of the emotional apparatus, or an intense furnace of contained explosiveness: the individual will have deadened feelings, or else too strong and disruptive ones. Either way, his life is greatly diminished in its richness, and full of painful experience.

The more contained or imprisoned the emotions are, the more the mind tends to focus upon them: 'ENERGY FOLLOWS THOUGHT', so when the mind focusses upon contained emotions, these are given energy, and stimulated, but not released from their imprisonment: the inner pressure further intensifies.

The gateways, or creative centres, must be gradually unlocked so that congested energy can flow out from the emotional centres, freeing the mind at the same time to become interested in matters outside the little world of the self.

We can aid this process in ourselves by getting more in contact with our physical body, and coaxing this back into a more connected relationship with Mother Earth and the nourishing vitality that Earth provides our bodies with for their maintenance: running, swimming, dancing, gardening, sports, crafts. These help us to re-connect through our bodies with the natural cycles of the Earth that we are subject to.

The mind ceases gradually from intensifying emotional experience by involving itself in mental activity that takes it beyond the confines of the little self: meditation, in order to gain some detachment from the clatter of day-to-day life and also to stimulate greater interaction with the source of all life, through one's own spiritual centre, the Soul; and also some study or mental interest which leads us nearer to a more creative participation in the lives of others.

Ever so gradually, in this way, our subtle bodies become clearer and free from distortion, till the Soul and spiritual frequency of energy can inspire and nourish and guide our earthly beings so that we then radiate a quality which is healing to others as well as enrichening to ourselves.

Figure 3

2. Duality Transforms into Trinity

The human state at this time is characterised primarily by duality. In other words, a state of balance, harmony or equilibrium is very difficult to experience, let alone consciously achieve. We fluctuate instead between feeling good or feeling bad, between figuring the way life ought to be according to our mental ideas, and experiencing the way it is in our hurt and turmoiled feelings. In striving to achieve equilibrium we will often blur our awareness by shutting off to our own distressed feelings and thoughts; sometimes we will use all kinds of physical aids to do this, e.g. cigarettes, stimulant drinks, sugar, alcohol, TV. This may help us to feel a sense of equilibrium which is really an illusion, and more like a deadening and numbing of our experience of the richness of life.

It is possible to achieve conscious equilibrium in a way which includes all opposites, even in their extreme manifestations, and therefore enriches the life, even though it may still involve turmoil. This pathway to equilibrium involves finding the third factor present in all circumstances, and learning to consciously work with this factor so that duality becomes trinity and is therefore harmonious. To discover and utilise this third factor, it is necessary to explore and know the different ways in which the opposites, or two aspects of duality, manifest and express themselves.

I want here to mention some aspects of duality, to hint at the ways in which they express themselves, and to point out the third factor and its working.

At a very abstract level we have the opposites of SPIRIT and MATTER. SPIRIT is very difficult to define. It is everywhere at once, yet always as one – it is non-separate; we know it as WILL – the will-to-be; it is the focussed, concentrated intention to exist . . . its action is SYNTHETIC (syn: same, thesis: design); . . . it draws all differentness into oneness. FIRE. Masculine. Electricity.

27

WALKING MEDITATION

Find a space where you feel comfortable. Bring your hands to the Heart centre, palms together, and take a few moments to make your connection, through your mind, with the Soul.

Our hands hang easily by our sides and we walk about, affirming as we go, the silver thread as our stabilising influence, and the Soul as our source of spiritual inspiration and strength. Although we are walking about in the world, we are inwardly maintaining harmony by scanning our inner bodies for stress and any build-up of tension. First of all, the spine; check this for balance and straightness; start at the hips — feel the spine resting easily between the hips — trace its position all the way up to the head. Notice areas you cannot connect with: these will be the most numbed with accumulated tension. Gently adjust the alignment of the spine in your mind's eye, as much as is possible without strain.

Check your shoulder-yoke for relaxedness; rotate the shoulder blades across the ribs to search for tension; shake it out gently through the arms. Now hip joints and legs; check each joint at the hips, knees and ankles, and assess the balance of each set of joints with each other. Test ankle and knee softness by feeling rainbows in your ankles and pink roses in your knees: with each step the rainbow springs you lightly upwards, and the roses open and close a little. Feel for tension in your neck and head; rotate your head gently in each direction and then feel it as a ball bobbing and drifting on the surface of a softly moving sea. Think of the lark which springs up and up into the azure sky, cascading her song of joy as she goes, and let your desire to be open to the Soul bound upwards also on wings of joy. The silver thread becomes more and more translucent, more and more vibrant, until you feel that this column of radiant love and light is the central reality of your being.

Reach up to the sun, physical symbol of the Soul, as it streams its vibrant rays of spiritual vitality upon us . . . reach down to the Earth, physical symbol of the body, the Mother who receives us and provides sustenance for our bodies. Bring the palms of the hands together at the Heart centre. The silver thread connects the Soul, high above us in spiritual space, with the Earth beneath our feet; it runs right through us, gently stabilises and harmonises us. We open our palms to receive the clear radiance flowing down towards us. We turn our palms down to receive the rich and steady nourishment emanating from the Earth up the thread. We bring the palms back to the Heart centre and then reach out with them to Humanity, at the same time skipping out into the world. We step out into the world with a gentle, easy motion, never losing our inner connection, via the silver thread, with the Soul above us or the Earth beneath us.

Walking Meditation

MATTER is everywhere on Earth; it is body, physicalness – intelligence acted out in FORM, always different, diverse, separate; we know it in all the shapes and forms around us, both animate and inanimate; it is the exploration of differentness – its action is individuality and SEPARATENESS . . . it affirms the infinite possibility of personality. EARTH. Feminine. Magnetism.

The third factor which relates these two is SOUL. Its nature is fluidity, harmony, equilibrium. It makes possible a creative RELATIONSHIP between these two opposites. Neither spirit nor matter have meaning in themselves; it is the relationship between them which provides the relevance, the purpose and the colour of life. It is the SOUL, then, which makes ONENESS possible, through providing a neutral medium through which SPIRIT can infuse MATTER, and through which, in turn, MATTER can be lifted up into SPIRIT. WATER. The Son. Interaction.

At a more dense, less abstract level, we can recognise the opposites of MIND and BODY.

MIND can be seen as a condensed expression of SPIRIT, and therefore has the qualities of FATHER, MASCULINE, ASSERTIVE, ACTIVE, OUTGOING. Mind is itself made up of two aspects: the lower concrete, or intellectual and personalised mind; and the higher abstract, or intuitive and impersonalised mind. The lower concrete mind deals with the material, physical and SEPARATIVE or analytical part of our life; whilst the higher abstract mind deals with the spiritual, SYNTHETIC, holistic part of our life. These two aspects need to be at-oned.

BODY is a specific and personal expression of MATTER and therefore has the qualities of MOTHER, FEMININE, RECEPTIVE, PASSIVE, INWARD. Its physical structure provides a mechanism for each of the aspects of trinity to express themselves through: brain for spirit, heart for Soul, and bony and muscular structure for matter.

The third factor which at-ones these opposites into a trinity is the emotional life, or body.

Mind and body meet in the emotional aspect and are enabled by it to interact with each other in harmonious flow. For most of us this harmonious flow is not possible simply because our emotional selves are choked up and numbed through much personal pain and trauma experienced in the course of our lives. This inhibits our personal enjoyment of life, but also the clogging of our personal fluidity means that the Soul cannot fully gain access to its vehicle of expression on Earth: our personality; so it is very difficult for us also, when in this state, to make conscious, usable contact with the spiritual side of ourselves. Just as mind is a condensed expression of spirit, so the emotional aspect is a more condensed expression of the soul, and so its task is to relate: it works through RELATIONSHIP; so when our emotional aspect is very clogged through much personal pain, it will be difficult for us to make satisfying relationships. Before we can truly fulfil ourselves through experiencing the flow of spirit down to Earth through the mechanism of our personalities, through relating spirit to matter and Earth, we need to dissolve and melt away the knots and tangles in our emotional selves; and only then can we experience real at-one-ment with and guidance from, the Soul, and consequent at-one-ment with all of life.

The third expression of duality that I want to mention here involves the opposites of LIVER and KIDNEYS, two essential organs within the body. The condition of these two organs within the physical body, and the relationship between them, directly affects the way in which an individual is able to carry out on Earth, through the medium of a physical body and a personality, that which he feels spiritually impelled towards. The functioning of these two organs can be seen as the base upon which the spiritual motivation rests; they are an expression of SPIRIT (FIRE AND AIR) and MATTER (EARTH AND WATER) at an even greater condensation.

Thus the role of the liver is to provide 'fire', or immediately usable energy whereby the body can carry out the will of the personal spirit. The liver condition reflects a person's capacity to assert himself, to be active and outgoing – it is masculine. Too much nervous tension or tightness in the liver will result in a person's flow of energy being spasmodic, irregular, jumpy and irritable; a stagnant and congested liver will result in depression, a sluggish attitude and responses – a sluggish digestion. Freeing the liver of both tension and congestion can result in a temporary sense of anger: if the individual expression (assertiveness) has been repeatedly inhibited and oppressed from an early age, the 'fiery' liver quality will be turned back upon the self and much negativity towards the self will result; when this is coaxed out, through liver congestion being etherically unravelled, some residue of congested fire will often need to be experienced and so the person will find himself feeling angry, apparently unreasonably. The antidote to this is to direct the anger, or fire, into a positive pursuance of one's personal life. So if you are recognis-

ing a need for more exercise to balance your lifestyle, get up and
go join a dance or swimming class, etc. . . or buy fresh vegetables
and put your assertive energy into making yourself a really
appetising salad.

Just as the liver is about outgoing and assertive, active energy,
so the kidneys are about incoming, receptive and passive energy,
and they correspond directly to the condition of water in the
individual. Their task is to filter the fluids of the body: they are
like the gravel on the bed of the stream, through which the water
flows before it collects in the pool at the bottom of the hill. The
condition of the kidneys directly affects the ease with which the
adrenal glands perform their task of making adrenalin available
for all physiological functions to be carried out. If the kidneys are
nervous, exhausted, or numbed, adrenalin will not be secreted in
a fluid or harmonious way, and so the liver production of energy
and the brain co-ordination of responses will be similarly lacking
in fluidity or harmony.

The liver responds directly to the kidney-adrenal state, even
though it is also influenced by other organs (e.g. pancreas, heart);
yet the kidney tangle cannot be fully unravelled before the liver.
Usually some superficial tension will be drained from the kidneys, enabling the liver to normalise somewhat; better liver
functioning will in turn enable the kidneys to relax at a deeper
level. Meanwhile changes will also be taking place in the flow of
energy through the thyroid, brain and heart: all parts of the body
influence each other always, for good and for bad. Kidney blocks
are usually the deepest and last that a person experiences in his
adjustment towards a clearer etheric vehicle and consequent
more direct contact with the Soul. Also, blocks in energy flow at
both liver and kidneys can be widely varying: acute, short-term
tension and tightness; if this continues for a long time it will
result in numbness and lack of response of any kind – genera-
lised, dulled functioning; congestion from long-term average
tension – this tends to be thick, cloudy, or sticky and sluggish.
The object whatever the condition is to improve flow through all
areas so that over-full areas are drained, and starved areas receive
nourishment.

It is the ovaries which make it possible for the liver and
kidneys to interact in a harmonious way: they (with the testes)
are the third factor enabling the energy of each to flow into the
other, and this interaction makes possible further growth
through form, either through the origination of another human

child, or through creative activity in the plane of Earth, carried out through the Base centre. Although ovarian and testicular activity does strongly influence our emotions, the role of WATER as the linking factor is less clear at this level of duality into trinity, because the kidneys govern the distribution of water in the body. Our physical bodies are largely made up of water, just as tension levels within them are controlled by the flow or constraint of our emotions. The kidneys, as the base organ in our bodies, are also predominantly to do with water. Energy flows through the ovaries in the form of a spiral; it is this spirallic action which enables the fire/air of the liver and the earth/water of the kidneys to connect harmoniously, thereby maintaining a balance and trinity which enables our spiritual identity to explore itself and grow through form and body upon Earth.

You will notice for yourself many more areas where opposite factors can be seen to be creating duality; if you seek more deeply into the dynamics of the situation you will recognise the third factor, the missing link which can create a trinity out of duality, and you can then apply your own personal energy towards aiding the functioning of this third factor and thereby stimulate a more harmonious relationship between the two opposing factors.

Here we have considered three levels at which duality and trinity can be seen functioning. Together the three form another example of duality: trinity at work, for the first group (SPIRIT: SOUL: MATTER) are purely abstract, intangible and invisible (SPIRIT); the third (LIVER: KIDNEYS: OVARIES) are very material, dense, tangible and visible, both in themselves and their functioning (BODY); whilst the middle group (MIND: EMOTION: BODY), when integrated in itself, works as the factor of RELATIONSHIP, or SOUL, bringing about a fluid interaction between that which is invisible and intangible, and that which is visible, tangible and real in the usual sense.

Thou who livest within my heart,
Awaken me to the immensity of Thy spirit,
To the experience of Thy living presence!
Deliver me from the bonds of desire,
From the slavery of small aims,
From the delusion of narrow egohood!

Enlighten me with the light of Thy wisdom,
Suffuse me with the radiance of Thy love,
Which includes and embraces the darkness,
Like the light which surrounds the dark
                    core of the flame,
Like the love of a mother that surrounds
The growing life in the darkness of the womb,
Like the earth protecting the tender germ
                    of the seed.

Let me be the seed of Thy living light!
Give me the strength to burst the sheath of
                    selfhood,
And like the seed which dies in order to be born,
Let me fearlessly go through the portals of death,
So that I may awaken to the greater life,
To the all-embracing life of Thy love,
To the all-embracing love of Thy
                    wisdom.

3. The Key of the Centres

Introduction

In this system of healing we are working at unravelling knots and tangles of energy in the etheric vehicle. Adjustment at the etheric level has a direct effect upon the nervous system and this enables problems of a physical, emotional, mental and spiritual nature to be corrected. The relationship between these four parts of our being is harmonised, making possible a better integration of each of them into the whole.

The Key which we use to interpret the messages received by our fingertips whilst working, is the Key of the Centres. This is an extremely accurate yet simple formula which makes it possible for us to relate an energy state in one place to the picture of the patient's whole state. We gain in this way a sense of the pattern of our patient's constitutional state, but also their current distortions. We can use this pattern to understand a patient's problems in their life-circumstances.

The centres (often called chakras) are located (in the etheric vehicle) in the area of the spinal cord. There are seven major centres; energy from the Divine Life is focussed by the centres, and transmitted from them to major glands in the body. The functioning of the glands is qualified by the condition of energy flow through the etheric centres, whilst the glands in turn condition, through their production and secretion of hormones, all the chemical activity in the body. The activity of the emotions and of the mind is strongly affected by the chemistry of the body, as is its physiological activity. If the body is toxic, from over-exposure perhaps to inorganic chemical substances in our water and our air, physical congestion will build up in the organs, and clog and slow down their efficiency; our emotions will also become turgid and our minds depressed. Similarly, if our minds are oppressed by too much dark or dreary thoughts, our hearts will become heavy and our body chemistry sluggish. The etheric vehicle becomes congested in both these circumstances, and when the etheric vehicle is congested, the flow of the Divine Life into our individual lives is inhibited and we lose our sense of perspective and our inspiration for life. This downward spiral is most quickly and efficiently adjusted by cleansing the etheric vehicle and thereby making possible a vital, strong flow of life force once more through the individual.

We rarely work directly upon the centres in the etheric vehicle, however, simply because their state and balance is very, very delicate and can best be adjusted by the Soul of the patient. Our work is to coax tensions away from the Strange Flow acupuncture points, and this enables congestion in the centres themselves to drain away. However, we apply the Key of the centres to our interpretation of the energy response in our patient, as received through our fingertips, as it is this Key which enables us to build up a pattern of understanding of his or her overall, and immediate state, and this understanding helps us to give subtle and sensitive aid as the problem unravels.

The Seven Centres and the Third Eye

(See chart 1)

The seven centres are:

The Crown centre (governing the Pineal gland).
The Third Eye centre (governing the Pituitary gland).
The Throat centre (governing the Thyroid gland).
The Heart centre (governing the Thymus gland).
The Solar Plexus centre (governing the Pancreas).
The Pelvic centre (governing the Ovaries and Testes).
The Base centre (governing the Adrenal glands).

These seven centres work in pairs, except for the Third Eye, which has a role all its own. Just as the Pituitary gland is the master or director of all the other glands in the body, so the Third Eye centre is the master of all the centres. It has very subtle functions, as it is the organ through which we learn to sense and know the invisible worlds; but it is also the organ we eventually learn to use as a projector of our own visions onto the world.

The goal we aim for is to hold our Crown centre (stimulating the Pineal gland) open to inspiration reaching it from the Soul; this inspiration is received by us as a wavelength: it is 'heard'. This sound wavelength is passed across to the Third Eye centre (stimulating the Pituitary gland) which converts it into an image, or visual form. This image is in turn projected, or transmitted, onto the world. In this way it is possible for us to create (in some small way!) our own world, and ideally the world we create through the projections of our Third Eye is inspired from the Soul and so is an effect of the emanations of the mind of God. This can only truly take place once the two 'eyes' of our mind, the intuition and the intellect, are focussed together.

The Lower Concrete and Higher Abstract Mind: The Two Eyes of the Mind

These two aspects of the mind are the two aspects of perception. The 'lower concrete mind', or intellect, works through the left brain, and the left eye is its external organ. It perceives and processes that which is outside us, in the 'concrete', visible, physical and material world around us. The 'higher abstract' mind, or intuition, works through the right brain, and the right eye is its external organ. It perceives, and processes that which is within us, in the 'abstract', invisible, subtle and non-physical world that we have access to through our minds.

These two organs enable us to perceive, explore and interact with the environment outside us, and the environment within us. Mostly there is a chasm between these two aspects of our experience and we feel alienation and disconnectedness as a result. To harmonise and integrate our two realities we need to be able to focus the two aspects of our organs of perception, the intuition and the intellect, together. When we can do this we make a quantum leap in consciousness; we break through a barrier and our experience and understanding become transformed; we begin to learn to use our Third Eye, for it is this organ in the etheric vehicle which focusses and harmonises the two mental activities of intellect and intuition.

It is also worth noting that the intellect is the organ of Knowledge, whilst the intuition is the organ of Wisdom. We can chase after information and facts all our lives, but it will never bring us contentment, or more than a fleeting sense of harmony with life, because information, facts and knowledge tell us only about the details in the picture of life; they cannot supply the thread that binds those parts into a whole or harmony. Knowledge tells us only about limitation, when all is said and done. However, the intuition, using the right brain, teaches us about the whole; it reveals to us a context in which the facts of our knowledge have perspective and deepened relevance and meaning because of this. If we have a context, we can find ourselves in the whole; we can fulfil an identity as part of a continuous, unfolding purpose; the details of our life take on new relevance in an enormous panorama of wonder.

The Six Centres as Three Pairs: The 'Bodies' of the Personality

(See chart 1)

The six other centres work in pairs, and each pair has a network of influence which can be conveniently described as a 'body'. Thus the two centres in the middle, the Solar Plexus and the Heart, form the emotional body; the centres to either side of the emotional body, the Pelvic and the Throat centres, can be described as the creative body (or organ of creative activity); and the centres at the top and bottom of the spine, the Base and the Crown, form the mental body.

Two Flows of Force: Active, or Masculine, Receptive or Feminine, Harmonised by Creative Activity

Each of these 'bodies' is animated by an active and a receptive flow of force, and in each body either the active or the receptive flow will dominate. This means that in the emotional body, the receptive flow is outermost, and therefore more obvious, whilst the active flow is innermost, and less obvious. In the mental body, the active, or masculine flow dominates, or is outermost, the feminine or receptive flow innermost. In the creative body neither dominates, for the creative centres are the gateways through which mental, emotional and physical activity flows in and out of one another. This means that the creative centres can be the most dynamic, yet they can also be the most inhibited and clogged of all the centres, and this is usually the case. When we seek to heal someone through adjusting the capacity for energy to flow through their system, we are primarily seeking to untangle the creative centres (Pelvic and Throat), so that the emotional and mental activity of the patient can once more find its way through the gateways of these centres and into expression (physical expression through the Pelvic centre, and the more subtle expression of the spirit through the Throat centre).

Whilst the emotional and mental bodies are predominantly receptive and active, or feminine and masculine, each of the two centres in each 'body' processes mainly active or receptive flows

THE CENTRES : CHART I

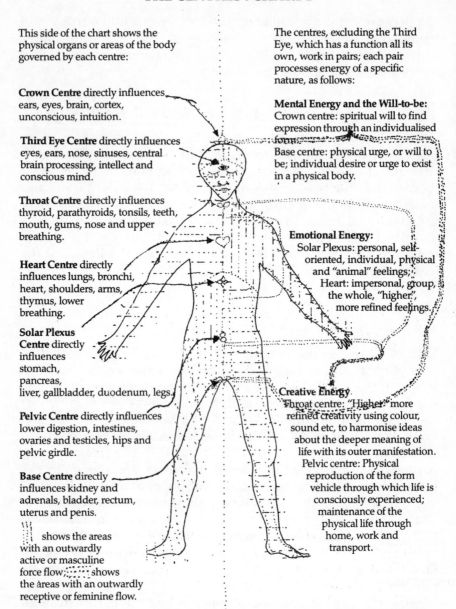

This side of the chart shows the physical organs or areas of the body governed by each centre:

Crown Centre directly influences ears, eyes, brain, cortex, unconscious, intuition.

Third Eye Centre directly influences eyes, ears, nose, sinuses, central brain processing, intellect and conscious mind.

Throat Centre directly influences thyroid, parathyroids, tonsils, teeth, mouth, gums, nose and upper breathing.

Heart Centre directly influences lungs, bronchi, heart, shoulders, arms, thymus, lower breathing.

Solar Plexus Centre directly influences stomach, pancreas, liver, gallbladder, duodenum, legs.

Pelvic Centre directly influences lower digestion, intestines, ovaries and testicles, hips and pelvic girdle.

Base Centre directly influences kidney and adrenals, bladder, rectum, uterus and penis.

⦙⦙⦙ shows the areas with an outwardly active or masculine force flow; ⋯⋯ shows the areas with an outwardly receptive or feminine flow.

The centres, excluding the Third Eye, which has a function all its own, work in pairs; each pair processes energy of a specific nature, as follows:

Mental Energy and the Will-to-be: Crown centre: spiritual will to find expression through an individualised form; Base centre: physical urge, or will to be; individual desire or urge to exist in a physical body.

Emotional Energy: Solar Plexus: personal, self-oriented, individual, physical and "animal" feelings; Heart: impersonal, group, the whole, "higher", more refined feelings.

Creative Energy: Throat centre: "Higher" more refined creativity using colour, sound etc, to harmonise ideas about the deeper meaning of life with its outer manifestation. Pelvic centre: Physical reproduction of the form vehicle through which life is consciously experienced; maintenance of the physical life through home, work and transport.

Left arm is outwardly emotional (feminine) but its emotions relate to the personal self and are therefore active and masculine. Right arm expresses emotions relating to others and the non-personal world. Left leg is outwardly mental, but the thoughts reflected here relate to the flow in from the Divine Life through the right, intuitive brain hemisphere and so are receptive and feminine. The right leg reflects the left brain: flow of active or masculine thought.

Chart I

of energy. Thus, the Solar Plexus centre is mostly active, whilst the Heart centre is mostly receptive; and the Base centre is mostly receptive whilst the Crown centre is mostly active. Our aim in seeking to achieve balance in our system is to have the receptive and active flows through our centres perfectly harmonised so that none dominates or is dominated by, any other flow. We achieve and maintain this ultimately through learning to focus our consciousness in the Soul. As healers, we aim to untangle and clarify knots and tangles in the etheric vehicle of the patient so that the Soul of the patient may achieve a better connection with his personality, or personal and earthbound self.

Centres below and above the Diaphragm

There is one further important point to remember concerning the relationships of the centres with each other. This concerns the centres below the diaphragm and those above it. The centres below the diaphragm (the Solar Plexus, Pelvic and Base) are all concerned with the maintenance of the body. They are stronger, more forceful and resilient than the higher centres. It is their task to maintain the body as a vital, dynamic, centred organism through which the mind can carry out into action, upon the Earth, the vision with which it is inspired by the Soul and the spiritual will. As we progress along our spiritual journey, we learn bit by bit to gather in the forces of our physical life, until they are concentrated in these centres; we learn to direct this physical force then according to our will as it is held receptive to the Soul, and so we resist the urge to dissipate, diffuse and scatter our physical force through purposeless activity.

This does not mean that we don't enjoy ourselves, for every experience in life has the capacity to enrich and therefore to bring joy; it simply means that we hold ourselves focussed into the particular pattern of flow intended for us at this time by our own Soul.

If we succeed in this concentration of the centres below the diaphragm, every action we make springs from this focussed-ness, and so each action is one-pointed, clear, and bound to bear fruit.

The energy carried by the centres above the diaphragm (the Heart, Throat, Third Eye and Crown) is much much more sensitive and delicate than that carried by the lower centres. Their function is to receive, interpret and express the energy flowing in from the Divine Life. This is expressed primarily through the Throat centre, and it is this centre which will always most strongly reflect any build-up of congestion in the upper body.

Be Tender with the Heart Centre!

The Heart centre is the most delicate of the centres at this time. It is therefore the most difficult to adjust because its sensitivity is so exquisite, it can too easily be unstabilised. It is under tremendous stimulation at this time of the planet as our minds encourage us to be more caring and more sharing towards others. The Heart centre is most sensitive to the Christ consciousness and to the will to give unconditional love. At this time there is an ache in the hearts of men and women across the world to end the strife and bloodshed, the hatred and aggression dividing the family of man. This yearning for harmony and peace exposes the Heart centre, opens it like a delicate, shy, hothouse blossom; yet, once opened, it is subjected to harshness, cruelty, the brutality and hypocrisy so present around us. This contrast of a tentative opening into a stormy environment puts enormous strain on this centre. For it to be able to encompass safely such extremes, it must be able to rest upon a firm and strong and focussed Solar Plexus. So, when we are adjusting our patient's energy, we work to clarify and strengthen the Solar Plexus, and to unravel and allow to drain away, congestion in the throat centre. We don't work directly upon the Heart centre as it is already exposed to enough stimulation and pressure from planetary and earthly forces. A strong and clear Solar Plexus and Throat centre will enable the Heart centre to be poised and open, firmly resting on the base of the Solar Plexus whilst steadily expressing itself through the Throat centre.

THE CENTRES OF THE EMOTIONAL BODY: HEART AND SOLAR PLEXUS

Our emotions, or feelings, form the basis upon which we experience our lives.

There are two aspects to our emotional body: our personal feeling, which deals with the detail of our individual existence (through this we are aware of difference or separation from

THE EMOTIONAL BODY & ITS CENTRES: HEART AND SOLAR PLEXUS CHART II

The Solar Plexus centre conditions primarily the upper abdomen and all its organs: stomach, pancreas, spleen, liver, gallbladder, duodenum. It also conditions the lower abdomen (and so also the related organs) and the legs and feet. It strongly influences the intellect or "lower concrete mind" and the left hemisphere of the brain.

It is the centre for the expression of the individuated, personal ego, for the sense of "I", or separated self. The condition of the Solar Plexus centre (as reflected through points used which connect with areas or organs governed by it) will immediately give clues as to the individual's relationship with himself.

A major function of this centre is the lifting of force from both the Pelvic and the Base centres up into itself, where it then organises and coordinates these, and its own, into a coherent pattern which governs the individual's personal, or "gut" feeling response to the world. Ideally it absorbs and digests the force of the base centre, the pelvic centre and its own, to produce active, "fiery" energy for the mobilising of the physical being into coherent action.

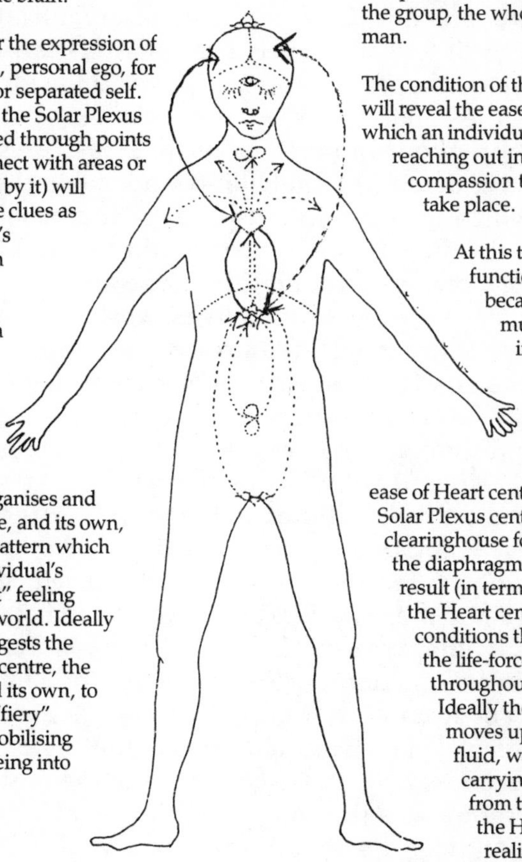

The Heart centre conditions primarily the area between the diaphragm and the throat and therefore the heart organ and the lungs! It also conditions the arms and hands, and shoulders and the intuitive or "higher abstract" mind, and the right hemisphere of the brain. It is the centre through which is expressed the identification with the group, the whole, the family of man.

The condition of the Heart centre will reveal the ease or difficulty with which an individual's spontaneous reaching out in oneness and compassion to the other can take place.

At this time this functioning is restricted because there is too much fear for individual security: this fear transmitted via the Solar Plexus centre locks up the ease of Heart centre flow. When the Solar Plexus centre has acted as clearinghouse for all force below the diaphragm, it then lifts the result (in terms of energy) up to the Heart centre, which in turn conditions the circulation of the life-force (blood-stream) throughout the system. Ideally the diaphragm moves up and down in a fluid, wave-like pulse, carrying this energy from the Solar Plexus to the Heart centre; in reality the movement of the diaphragm is uneven because of lack of vitality at the Solar Plexus centre: poor absorption and elimination of gut feeling.

*When seeking to work out in your mind the relationships between the outward and inward flows of active – masculine, and receptive – feminine force, please bear in mind that the blue, active and masculine force always strongly influences and reflects the personal ego, whereas the pink, receptive and feminine force always strongly reflects and influences the impersonal, the life beyond the little self.

Chart II

others); and our impersonal feeling, which deals with our deeper sense of oneness with the whole of creation.

The condition of our personal feeling, as expressed via the Solar Plexus centre will determine the vitality and balance of our whole physical system. The emotions carried through this centre are primarily anger (liver), jealousy (gall-bladder), nervous irritability (pancreas), impatience (stomach). However, it also is powerfully affected by the condition of both the Pelvic and the Base centres, because it has to lift up and organise the force of these centres. So it will also reflect the emotions carried by these centres: i.e. fear (the Base centre, kidneys and adrenals); and sexual desire (the Pelvic centre).

The condition of our impersonal feeling, as expressed via the Heart centre will determine the vitality and stable rhythm of our circulation, which includes the inspiration and exhalation of air and therefore the distribution of oxygen through the system.

The emotions carried through this centre are compassion, joy, sense of oneness with all of life; (it is worth noting here that when the heart centre is well-matured the individual will find it very difficult to condemn another person, for whatever reason); the Heart centre also carries nervous anxiety, hurt, isolation. The emotional condition of worry results from an unstable interaction between the Heart and Solar Plexus centres.

The emotions above attributed to the Solar Plexus centre result when one reacts emotionally to the activity of others. If these personal emotional reactions can be neutralised, or burnt of waste products, by the solar Plexus centre, the remaining force is that of the outgoing, creative fire of life. This is the task of the Solar Plexus in its function of clearing-house for all force carried by itself, the Pelvic and Base centres: to *assimilate* emotional gut experience, *eliminate* its unwanted aspects and thereby to release the vital and fearless *will to live* for the use of the higher centres.

The Heart centre acts through a 'melting away', rather than a 'burning off', of dross. Purified Solar Plexus vitality is passed up to it via the diaphragm, and spiritual will is breathed into it via the Crown centre and the intuitive or higher abstract mind. The meeting of these two extremely potent forces, at the Heart centre, causes a melting away of hurt and anxiety, and a steady radiance, instead, of compassion and joy.

This unfoldment of the Heart centre can only come about through the inflow of spiritual will via the Crown centre and the intuitive faculty. No matter how advanced and brilliant the intellect or the Third Eye centre, these subtle organs cannot bring about the maturing of the Heart centre. This is an important consideration because there are many people today with extremely advanced intellects, who are highly knowledgeable and versed in the ancient wisdom and the occult, yet whose Heart centres are not maturing because they are working via the intellect without the balance of inflow from the Crown centre, and therefore from the Divine Life.

At this time there is tremendous confusion in the relationship between these two centres, in both individuals but also in the whole world. We know that we need to be more caring and more sharing; these ideals influence us at the mental level; so there is pressure upon our Heart centres to open and radiate love and compassion. But on the whole the energy made available to the Heart centre from the Solar Plexus is laden with fear, anger, impatience and grief. So there is dark and congested energy offered up to the Heart centre – poor material with which to produce clear radiance; whilst the Solar Plexus itself is too fragile and weak to provide the strength with which to carry out into action the caring and sharing which the heart desires.

The transmission of force between these two is in turmoil. Equally in the whole world, we know that if we are to survive we have to work together as one human family to share the resources of the planet in a more balanced way; yet we are still too insecure, too afraid that if we give generously we will be exploited or lose our individuality.

THE GATEWAY CENTRES: THROAT AND PELVIS

The Pelvic and the Throat centres deal with creative energy. 'Creative' stems from the Latin, creare, which means to create, produce, beget, bring forth; and from the French, creistre, and croître, meaning to increase, or grow. So creativity is about producing, about bringing forth, about increasing and growing.

This is important because these two centres do not form a body in the sense that the two emotional or feeling centres form the emotional body, or that the Base and Crown centres form the mental body. This is because these two centres are gateways; they are keys; they play a role of linking, bridging and integrating the energy of the other two pairs of centres.

To perform their role of bridge, or gateway, these centres need

THE CREATIVE CENTRES: THROAT & PELVIS
CHART III

The Pelvic centre conditions all the functions of the lower abdomen: lower digestion and intestines, ovaries, testicles, hips and pelvic girdle. The closeness of this centre to the Base centre means that the two influence and overlap each other to a large extent. This can at times cause confusion. This is particularly so in terms of the testes and ovaries; both are influenced by both Base and Pelvic centres but the testes more strongly by the Base centre whereas the ovaries more strongly by the Pelvic centre.

The pelvic is the centre which determines an individual's drive to create in physical and material terms. It primarily determines therefore, the bringing together of the twofold elements of male and female in order to bring about unity in the form of a new individual. Sexuality is the most obvious expression of this centre, but it is also expressed through physical work with the elements of earth. So building, farming, all crafts to do with maintaining physical life upon earth, and also all to do with transport (mobility of our physical bodies through the field of life), all work which involves expressing ideas through matter (or spirit – masculine through matter – feminine) uses this centre.

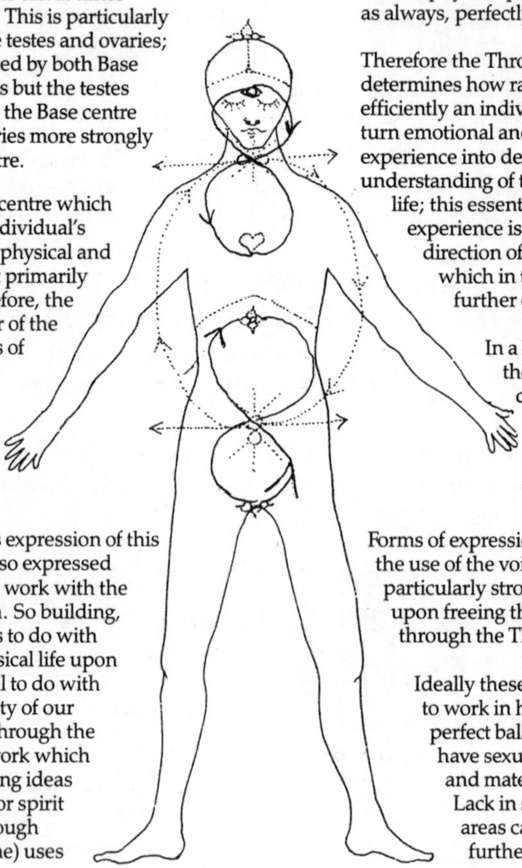

The Throat centre conditions primarily the thyroid and through it the speed at which an individual system converts available material into fuel for further growth and development. This is most obvious in terms of physical metabolic rate, but the physical pattern corresponds as always, perfectly with the subtle.

Therefore the Throat centre determines how rapidly and efficiently an individual is able to turn emotional and mental experience into deeper understanding of the meaning of life; this essential extract of experience is then used for the direction of further growth which in turn brings further experience.

In a less abstract sense the Throat centre is to do with all forms of creative expres- sion: music, song, dance, painting, drama. Forms of expression which include the use of the voice have a particularly strong influence upon freeing the flow of energy through the Throat centre.

Ideally these two centres need to work in harmony. For perfect balance we need to have sexual and physical and material expression. Lack in some of these areas can stimulate further activity in other areas.

Chart III

to be open, with energy flowing very freely through them. We know only too well that this is rarely the case. Repressed sexuality locks the gate of the Pelvic centre which often influences the Throat centre in such a way that a person cannot seem to express his less material, artistic urges.

Ideally, these two centres are the key to a life moving ever onward and into fresh dimensions of experience. When the Pelvic centre is open and vital, the base energy of the individual's will to live, at the Base centre, is successfully integrated and harmonised with his personal feeling response to life at the Solar Plexus centre, so that he is able to move outwards in the physical dimension of his life in such a way that the endless variability and richness of the physical plane is expressed through his personal activity. The things which particularly come under this category are all aspects of home maintenance: building, decorating, interior design, carpentry, sewing, gardening: any physical activity which adapts or adjusts the physical environment according to a person's feelings and ideas, and for the maintenance of his physical existence.

When the Throat centre is open and vital, the energy of the Heart centre (which includes the harmonically absorbed energy released from the Solar Plexus centre into the Heart centre), is successfully integrated and harmonised with the energy of the mental body. The energy of the mental body involves the harmonic integration of three centres (the Crown, the Third Eye and the Alta Major, governing the carotid gland), but to avoid confusion at this stage it is best if we think simply in terms of mental, or thought energy.

So the Throat centre is the gateway, or Key, through which our emotional experience in life is harmonised with our thinking, with our ideas. When a person is locked into a sense of separation from the rest of life, his ideas will reflect this. He will say to himself: 'Nobody else is going to respect my needs, so I must make sure I get what I want, even if it means ignoring my neighbours' needs'. This is a predominant mental attitude throughout the world.

However, when a person is strongly identified with a sense of the oneness of life, his mind is probably open more to influence from the mind of God, or the Divine Life, than from a personal desire for survival. His mind will 'breathe in' inspiration from the mind of the Divine Life, and this will intermingle with his experience in the emotional dimension, so that his creativity will be deeply to do with growth, with bringing forth; it will lead him ever onwards and outwards.

Expression via this centre is more to do with less material or functional media: music, song, dance, visual arts, etc: expression which nourishes and enriches the human spirit but is not essential for the maintenance of the human body.

The important thing to remember about these two centres is that they harmonise and integrate the masculine and feminine, active and receptive aspects of force, into a whole, or a unity or balance.

Thus the Pelvic centre brings together the Solar Plexus and the Base centres, masculine and feminine aspects of the densest, most physical part of our being; whilst the Throat centre brings together the emotional and the mental, feminine and masculine, aspects of the more subtle, less physical or dense parts of our being. The unity produced through these harmonic integrations forms the essence of new development and growth.

THE CENTRES OF MIND OR WILL : THE CROWN AND THE BASE

The Crown centre and the Base centre are linked through the energy of will. At the Crown this is expressed as the will of the Divine Life, the will of the whole, the will of the Spirit. At the Base centre it is expressed as the will of the individual, the individual urge or desire to live. As the individual evolves he has gradually to bring these two aspects of the will into at-one-ment. The end result of this is that the desire of the individual for life is surrendered consciously to the desire of the Divine Life for its expression through the individual. The individual will becomes overshadowed by the will of the greater, by the intelligence of the whole. The individual life is encompassed by the Divine Life. This does not mean that we lose our sense of personal existence; but that the personal existence is motivated by the Divine existence. In effect, the result is that the individual finds that activity towards the good of the whole becomes activity which encompasses and expresses also the good of himself.

All people who are drawn towards work involved in caring for the good of others are moving towards a richer, more fluid exchange of energy between these two centres. Another signifi-cant point is that a period of intense pain and difficulty inevita-

THE MENTAL BODY & THE CENTRES OF WILL: CROWN & BASE
CHART IV

The Base centre has an influence upon all the functions of the lower abdomen, but in particular the rectum and testes in a man, the rectum and womb in a woman; the organ specifically linked with the Base centre is the kidney and adrenal gland.

The Base is the centre which determines an individual's will to be, or exist. It will therefore have a bearing on a person's competitive drive; and someone who lives reluctantly, or even has a suicidal tendency, will have a constriction of flow of energy at the Base centre. The fluidity with which energy circulates through the Base centre will in turn influence the vitality at the Solar Plexus centre to which a person has access, so it will affect the whole of a person's physical dynamism.

Fear is at the root of all stuck emotional activity, and fear is the specific emotion linked with the Base centre and stored as tension at its organ: the kidney and adrenal gland. If one is reluctant, through fear, to go forward into one's life, the secretion of adrenalin will be inadequate and so numerous other chemical changes will not take place with the resonance necessary for one to have a fit mechanism with which to fulfill one's purpose.

The Crown centre conditions primarily the pineal gland, and therefore also the functioning of the intuition and the higher, abstract mind. It has a strong influence upon both eyes and ears, both seeing and hearing; but it influences the ears, and hearing, more strongly than the eyes. Its special function is to resonate to the spiritual plane and to relay the abstract information received from there into images which can be converted themselves into terms which are usable and communicable at the tangible, wordly level of day-to-day life.

For many people this centre is not functioning at all; for others it is functioning but its activity is unconscious and so may not readily be coordinated; for yet others this centre is very active but this activity is blocked from access to the rest of the mechanism. This last situation inevitably causes serious energy problems as the Crown centre activity is extremely stimulating but this stimulation is not being expressed, and so causes congestion.

For this centre to fulfil itself the Third Eye centre needs also to be quite developed as it is mostly through the Third Eye centre that the crown centre can convert its abstract activity into communicable terms.

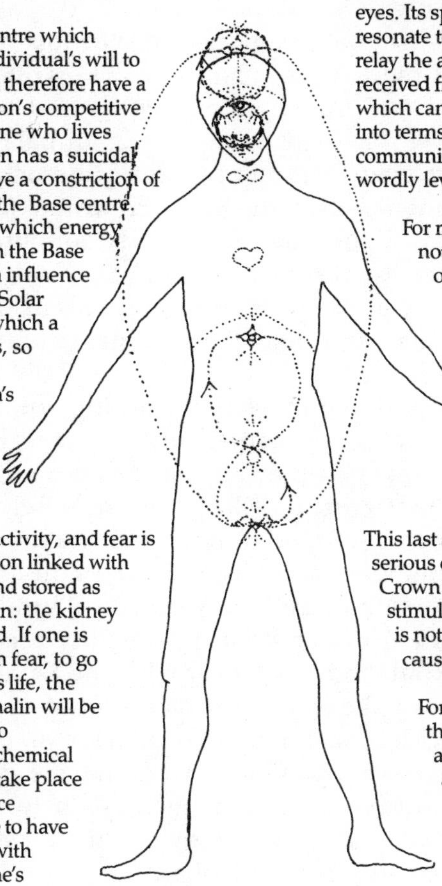

Chart IV

bly precedes the further at-one-ment of these two centres. The pain is experienced by the individual consciousness as it is pushed towards a greater relinquishment or surrender to the Divine Will. Pain will produce in the individual either bitterness and resentment, or a striving towards divine understanding and the deeper significance of life.

It is fear which holds us back from complete surrender to the Divine Will. We fear loss of self, extinction. It is necessary to acknowledge this fear, to allow it to be, like all our other 'negative' emotions, yet not to act upon it. We must be careful not to pretend it is not there, or to push it out of sight, for if this is done it will continue to influence our action and being from a subtle level; yet we have to avoid being unbalanced by its presence. The only way that this can really be achieved is by maintaining alignment with the Soul. So when fear seeks to influence us, we must turn our eyes, and therefore the mind, upwards, away from the fear and towards the Soul, the focus of love and light, or focus of spiritual energy. From this point of concentration we act, and make decisions, and observe the situation – the fear as well.

When a person is drawn towards working for the good of others, yet is held back from further fulfilling this, by fear, it is important for that person then to seriously work upon his relationship with the spiritual plane, or the Divine Life. His point of evolution has equipped him with the faculties necessary to begin to serve humanity according to the will of the Divine Life. But fear will inevitably be a very powerful hindrance to his further development. Development of a readily-accessible relationship with the Soul, and through it with the Divine Life, will give us an anchor in the enormity of spiritual space, a firm, reliable holdfast which will help us to achieve poise at the worldly, day-to-day level, no matter what storms may seem to rage. Also, this spiritual anchorage enables us to contact and channel Divine Love and this energy is the most cleansing, revitalising, healing and stabilising of any.

As an improved flow of energy takes place between these two centres, the person will find himself much more immediately aware of what direction or action he should take, both in situations concerning his innermost, personal life, and situations concerning his role in the wider, less personal world.

These two centres together can be described as the mental body because their fundamental energy is that of will, which is also the foundation of mind: it is the most abstract yet essential nature of mind, the basic urge to be, and to exist.

The Crown centre processes will, or mind, at its most abstract which is also the primary link of human consciousness with Divine consciousness; whereas the Base centre processes will, or mind, at its most dense, its most earthed. There is a continuous magnetic tension and interplay between these two centres which in time enables a human being to coherently ground and express spiritual and extraterrestial force through the planetary condition of Earth.

The Crown centre, however, to truly fulfil its potential, must include in itself the Third Eye and Alta Major centres. Together, these three centres for the balancing of energy, form the higher aspect of mind.

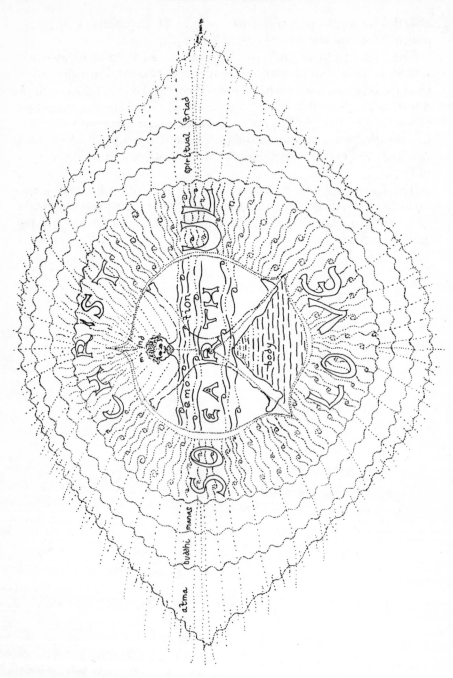

Figure 4

4. Cycles of Tension-gathering, Cycles of Tension-release

We exist in a universal plane of moving energy, which is made up of three elements: Spirit, or air, which is energy moving at its fastest; Body, or earth, which is energy moving at its slowest; and the element of Love, or water, which has the task of balancing and harmonising and integrating the other two.

When the third element of Love is not present, the other two, Spirit and Body (or matter), oppose each other in a raw and abrasive way and a state of duality affects both. Spirit can be described as the activity of will and this will has the intention to produce, or bring about something. It seeks to fulfil its idea or plan in the realm of matter, or Earth. This effort to build or create in matter, upon Earth, results in a continuous urge towards the future; it results in a progressive, onward pattern of movement. All life existing in our universe is subject to this progressive, onward movement.

When the element of Love is not active and flowing, Spirit and Matter are in a state of duality; they are unable to move forward in a harmonious or coherent way. There is an element of destruction present resulting from the friction which builds up between them. When Love once more flows between them, their interaction is able to follow a progressive pattern of onward movement, and this will result in the emergence of cycles. Each cycle will always to some extent repeat the previous cycle and will always pass through a peak and a lull. At the peak, the Spirit, air and high frequency motion of energy will dominate; whilst at the lull, the Body, earth and slow frequency motion of energy will dominate.

The cyclic pattern of movement is at its most progressive and dynamic when it becomes a spiral. When this happens each cycle is quite visible and apparent to the life living it and as each cycle is completed it moves up a tone or a shade so that although the

51

next cycle will still repeat the same basic pattern of the previous one, it will do so at a higher frequency. So when the spiral begins it emits a deep, slow note, but as it climbs higher and higher its note becomes faster and lighter.

Love will circulate more freely through and out from this spiral and it will radiate light into its environment.

This pattern is a universal law which governs the elemental energy from which all life springs. This means that all forms of life upon Earth, including ourselves, are subject to this pattern of energy flow.

The more we can recognise the cycles in our lives, accept them, love them, and seek to work in harmony with them, the more we find ourselves in tune with the Divine Spirit itself, and the Plan which the Spirit seeks to make visible and tangible and manifest in Matter, upon Earth.

Part of present day distress and dis-ease is caused by our effort to remove cycles from our lives; rather than being pliable and adaptable to the changing cycles of Nature, we try to eradicate their effects upon us by centrally heated homes and transport systems, and shopping centres. We lose touch then with the impact of the fundamental seasons of Nature upon our inner moods and personal cycles. Within each year there are seasons, within each season, months, within each month weeks and within each week, days. Within each day there are the cycles of night moving through dawn into day and then dropping back down again through dusk into night. We resist the flow of this cycle by artificial light, and by stimulants such as coffee, tea and sugar which press our systems into going at a faster rate than our natural daily cycle is in harmony with.

These cycles of the body through its natural source, Mother Earth and her planets, have as companions subtler cycles which involve the emotions and the Soul within each one of us. These are the moods of the heart, which dip and lift through winter and summer, night and day, following a cyclic pattern in harmony with the cycles of the body. Having disturbed our sense of our bodily cycles we have also disturbed these subtler cycles, so that our moods and emotions tend to be disjointed and haywire, unable to connect easily with the moods and emotions of others.

It is these subtler cycles of mood and emotion which should express in a day-to-day, well-grounded way, Love, or that element which enables a frictional state of duality to flow into a harmonious cycle. Because our connectedness with these cycles is disrupted, our thought-life becomes cut off and isolated and cannot find any way whereby it may flow down through our feelings and bodies and into our journey upon Earth. Our minds become wandering, homeless vagrants, and sometimes vandals, seeking to gain some kind of anchorage in the lives and realities of others.

This is a condition of destruction, of incoherence, where nothing fits together with anything else and life loses its meaning; it is a situation of duality, in which the Spirit part of our beings is not connected harmoniously with our bodies, and friction exists between the two.

How can we influence our lives so that the critical state of duality can become a moving state of trinity in which love carries us through our cycles with understanding and fluidity; and eventually into the highly creative state of spirallic progression?

We have traced how the blocking of the activity of love brought a state of duality, so our aim is to get love moving once more through the arenas of life that lack it. Love is always present, being a fundamental element underlying all life. The task is to get it moving. It stops moving when feelings have no outlet; in other words, when there is no means to express in terms of our feelings what we are experiencing. So we need to explore ways through which our feelings can be expressed.

In the course of a lifetime, we find ourselves in many experiences which are unpleasant, full of conflict, and very challenging to our sense of personal safety, security, and peace of mind. These experiences disturb our emotional equilibrium and set up tension within us, which, if not freed and expelled very soon, becomes fixed into the cell tissue of our bodies, affecting both nerves and muscles throughout our system. If this tension remains without being cleared before the next difficult period in our life happens, it becomes more rigid and a new layer of tension is laid down on top of it from the current trauma that is taking place.

For someone whose life is a continuous series of stressful circumstances, especially if he or she is very sensitive and feels things deeply and acutely, these bands of tension will soon form a closeknit web of subtle but imprisoning substance which will prevent him or her from responding to life in a spontaneous or relaxed way. There will tend to be a strong fear of more trauma, and this fear will cause the bands of tension to be held as a shield between the everyday world and the real, but caged, inner spirit.

The degree of rigidity and depth of these bands of tension will vary between individuals, depending upon their constitutional nature and the experience that has come their way. But the fundamental pattern remains the same for all of us: bands of tension causing congestion of the flow of energy through us, and also distortion of our capacity to express our inner spirit.

The aim of life, whether we realise it or not, is always for the Divine Spirit to express itself through the varied forms which our personalities make available to it. We do not experience atonement or peace until this union between the Divine and the individual comes about. Anyone who seeks healing is really seeking to draw nearer to this union.

It is the bands of tension built up around us which slow and distorts the flow of the loving spirit through us, fixing us into an experience of life as duality, and blocking us off from its cyclic flow.

When we use Jin Shin Do to heal, we are manipulating electro-magnetic forcefields in order to stimulate a melting away of the bands of tension, so that the Divine Spirit may flow more freely and with less distortion through the patient.

Our hands work magnetically, whilst our minds work electrically. The two are active simultaneously. The magnetic force of the hands draws the outermost layer of tension away from the patient. At the same time our mind is attuned to the rhythm of the Soul (concentrating the Love aspect of the Universal Life), thereby opening up a channel whereby Soulforce may flow more readily than it otherwise could.

The healer does not absorb the tension he is magnetically drawing away from the patient so long as he maintains his attunement to the rhythm of the Soul, because the force of the Soul sets up a vibration around him which purifies and expels poisons through mental, emotional and physical bodies. This Soul connection is the healer's protection whilst working.

The outermost layer of tension is the most accessible, and the most readily shiftable because it has not had a chance as yet to become rigid or crystallised. It is not possible to reach the deeper layers before the outer layer has been removed . . . we have to work our way steadily backwards, gradually melting away superficial layers of tension until we reach a core band. This will have resulted from a particularly fundamental and powerful experience of trauma.

But the work of the hands is strengthened and intensified by the work of the head. As a stronger flow of Soulforce pours into the patient because of the mental attunement of the healer, this force pushes at the bands of tension from within, and so gradually nudges them closer to the surface or more within the magnetic forcefield of the hands. Thus there is a two-way activity taking place all the time. Also, as the bands of tension are drawn off, and the inner presence of Soulforce strengthens, the patient feels more in control, more in touch with life processes within and without himself, and therefore is better able to take steps in his own life to aid the healing process.

We have described the inflow of Soulforce as a rhythm; this rhythm can also be described as a pulse and as a wave. The rhythm, pulse or wave is the way in which we experience the cycle of Soulforce as it flows through us. If we are imprisoned in an awareness only of duality in our lives, we will be unable to feel this pulse, wave, or rhythm. When we are healed, or enabled to experience life more whole, the circulation of Soulforce and Love becomes stronger in our veins and we begin to be sensitive to the cyclic flow of lifeforce through us and can then recognise and be tuned to this rhythm of cycles.

Within each of us the inflowing Soulforce is governed by the state of the seven centres in the etheric vehicle. These transmit the Life energy to the major glands of the body, and these glands in turn produce hormones which cause all the bodily functions to be carried out. The glands will not work properly if energy is not flowing in an orderly, rhythmic fashion, from the etheric centres, and if the glands are not working properly the hormonal production will be unbalanced and all the chemical interactions necessary for the health and vitality of the body will be disturbed. The body will not be synchronised to its own spiritual essence, or to its environment and it will be in a state of dis-ease. If my body is out of tune in this way, my spiritual essence will be limited in its capacity to express itself through that body and I will experience negativity, anxiety, depression and fear – emotions which block and inhibit the fulfilment of my spiritual destiny.

In most of us the tension which blocks the cyclic flow of energy through the centres builds up around a basic pattern.

It usually stems from a lack of circulation in the emotional centres, so we seek to encourage better flow through these centres. There is no point in encouraging circulation unless that which is got moving has somewhere to go. We must then make sure that the points of outlet, or expression, are loosening and

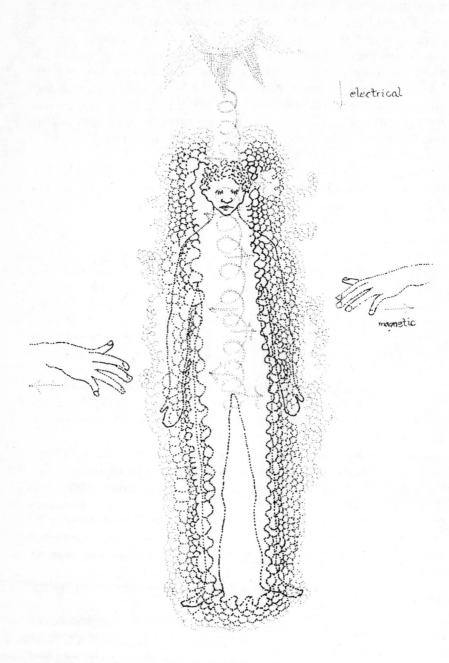

electrical

magnetic

Figure 5

freeing, so that the emotions as they begin to move can find channels to flow through. Actually it is rarely appropriate to work directly upon the emotional centres. The Solar Plexus can be quite explosive, whilst the Heart is always very delicate and vulnerable. But if we can loosen up the Pelvic and Throat centres, to either side of the Heart and Solar Plexus, and which have the job of expression, it becomes possible for congested emotion to find its way out and away, leaving room for fresher, cleaner emotional activity.

The electro-magnetic work of the healer can stimulate a cleansing at the etheric level, but for this to be maintained it will become necessary for the patient to explore the doorways in his life for self-expression. Where Pelvic congestion is concerned, this will involve re-assessing the home, career, craft, sport and sexuality areas of the life; where throat congestion is concerned, outlets of expression through song, music, art and healing need exploring. Music, song and dance are the purest means to freeing emotional congestion. Song enables the sorrows and joys of the Heart centre to be poured out and shared in a community group with the sorrows and joys of mankind, whilst dance enables a stuck Pelvis to loosen and free so that frustrated feeling at the Solar Plexus can be tapped or stamped or stepped out rhythmically into the Earth; music itself enables the feelings of both Solar Plexus and Heart to soar up to at-one with the Spirit, and to use this contact to inspire and rejuvenate the personality.

We easily become entangled in our own emotional confusion in this age of relative freedom from physical activity, lack of a natural relationship with God, and emphasis upon therapy. The pool of our emotions silts up and grows stickier and less fluid the more we focus narcissitically upon the gruesome details of our emotional progress through life. The powerful solvents of Soulforce and community sharing and activity will be needed to dissolve away this stickiness. And in time the person will need to become part of a network of people who provide him with both the emotional sharing and caring he or she was deprived of at an early age, and also, a function and place as a useful, contributing member of a community.

When Soulforce flows easily into our beings it stimulates first the right hemisphere of the brain, then is passed across, via the corpus callosum, to the left hemisphere. It passes from the head through the Throat centre to the Heart centre. From here it is passed across the diaphragm to the Solar Plexus, through the

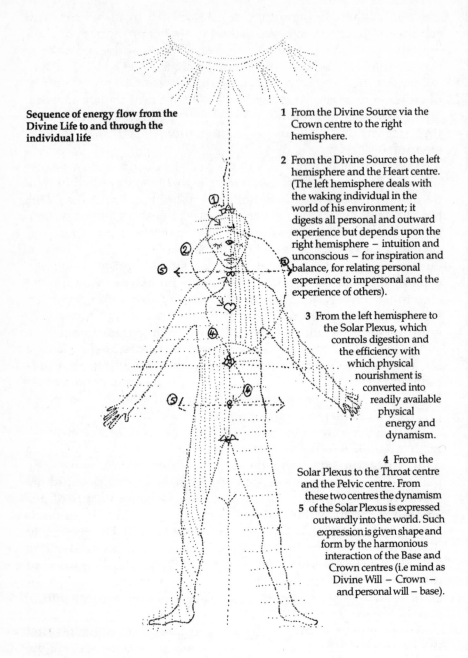

Sequence of energy flow from the Divine Life to and through the individual life

1 From the Divine Source via the Crown centre to the right hemisphere.

2 From the Divine Source to the left hemisphere and the Heart centre. (The left hemisphere deals with the waking individual in the world of his environment; it digests all personal and outward experience but depends upon the right hemisphere – intuition and unconscious – for inspiration and balance, for relating personal experience to impersonal and the experience of others).

3 From the left hemisphere to the Solar Plexus, which controls digestion and the efficiency with which physical nourishment is converted into readily available physical energy and dynamism.

4 From the Solar Plexus to the Throat centre and the Pelvic centre. From these two centres the dynamism
5 of the Solar Plexus is expressed outwardly into the world. Such expression is given shape and form by the harmonious interaction of the Base and Crown centres (i.e mind as Divine Will – Crown – and personal will – base).

Figure 6

Pelvic centre to the Base centre. Bands of tension will block first the Solar Plexus, which is responsible for the maintenance of our selfhood in a physical body. This will immediately affect our digestion and so also our physical vitality. If it is not quickly cleared, but suppressed or masked, it will steadily influence our left brain functioning, making this nervous, tense, brittle, sticky and eventually either dulled or aggressive.

At the same time, the memory of the event which caused the original tension and unhappiness will be buried deep in our unconscious right brain. From here it will influence the activity of our Heart centre, holding it contained and stiff in its ability to open flowingly into the lives of others.

Clogging of the right brain will restrict the reception of inflow via the Crown centre (Divine inspiration) and will have a similar reflex action of constraint upon the Base centre (personal will to carry out the inspiration). Energy needs to flow between these two centres, (as between the other pairs of centres) with a cyclic motion, involving both peak and lull, and all the phases in between.

As more unhappy experience comes our way, further bands of tension build up around our etheric centres, dulling more and more the inflow of Soulforce. The channels of expression, the Throat and Pelvic centres, will become stiffer and stiffer and the different parts of the self will become disconnected from each other. We may recognise our lack of wholeness, and will to remedy the situation (this recognition is an activity of the Crown centre working with the Third Eye centre), but undoubtedly our Pelvis is stuck and so very little energy is reaching the Base (the centre responsible for carrying out into action that which we will to do), and so we lack the mechanism to fulfil our will. This is a more frustrating state to be in than that in which we are very lacking in wholeness, but unaware of it. However, our frustration will eventually become so unbearable that we will seek help, and, in time, find the right person to help our problem.

The more the right brain fills up with unhappy memories buried deep, the more we lose contact with our deeper, inward, spiritual essence and the more we have to devise ways of relating to others in our day-to-day lives, which protect us from exposure to our own inner pain. These masks defend us from too much shock in the world, but also become a prison which prevents an easy, spontaneous response to the cycles in our own lives and those of others.

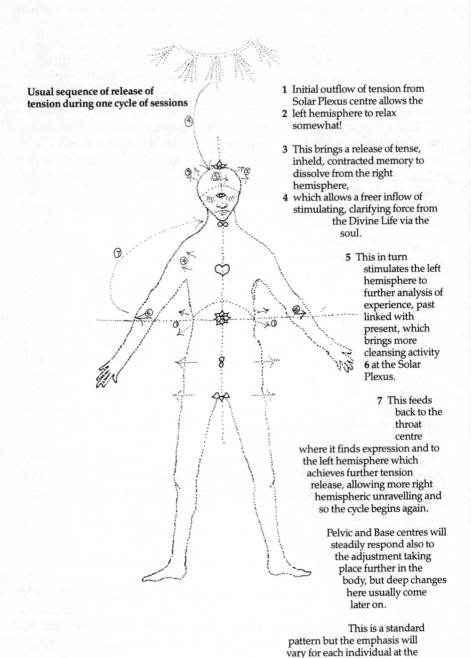

**Usual sequence of release of
tension during one cycle of sessions**

1 Initial outflow of tension from
  Solar Plexus centre allows the
2 left hemisphere to relax
  somewhat!

3 This brings a release of tense,
  inheld, contracted memory to
  dissolve from the right
  hemisphere,
4 which allows a freer inflow of
  stimulating, clarifying force from
  the Divine Life via the
  soul.

5 This in turn
  stimulates the left
  hemisphere to
  further analysis of
  experience, past
  linked with
  present, which
  brings more
  cleansing activity
6 at the Solar
  Plexus.

7 This feeds
  back to the
  throat
  centre
where it finds expression and to
the left hemisphere which
achieves further tension
release, allowing more right
hemispheric unravelling and
so the cycle begins again.

Pelvic and Base centres will
steadily respond also to
the adjustment taking
place further in the
body, but deep changes
here usually come
later on.

This is a standard
pattern but the emphasis will
vary for each individual at the
different stages, depending on the
central focus for acute tension.

Figure 7

In unravelling these bands of tension, we gently loosen the Throat and Pelvis, enabling energy to circulate more freely throughout the system. This renewed circulation will wash up to the surface the remains of past un-dealt-with experience at all levels. This will usually be recognisable in a physical, emotional and mental form and it will often follow a specific pattern, although this is not always the case.

This pattern begins with the Solar Plexus, usually the most obviously polluted of the centres, and at the hub of our experience of our personal life.

First the healer loosens the offending tension. This can bring an immediate sense of release or ease. This ease allows the nervous system to rest and gain some strength and resilience so it will be able to cope with the deeper bands of congestion as they surface. It is not possible for these deeper bands to release until the nervous system is strong enough to be able to deal with the shock of confrontation with past memories which release usually brings, and this is a natural safety-valve or mechanism which it is unwise to tamper with. It is pointless to seek to force, through any method, a release of old tension before we are emotionally and psychologically strong and clear enough to deal with it. We cannot progress or grow if we are unable to deal with what is emerging. The healer's task is simply to ease current tension away gently, allowing rest from overwhelming stress, and time, to do the rest.

The initial release will allow a loosening of the layer of tension contained beneath it; the loosening will be followed, when the person is ready, by a surfacing. This surfacing can bring a sense of self-confrontation and shock with it, but it does not always do so. Sometimes no unhappiness or trauma or unwanted memory takes place, simply a fresh understanding of the events of one's life, and a sense of shedding unneeded dross. The mind will be beginning to clear at this point, and it will re-order what it remembers, arranging things in the new light of fresh experience and understanding. We will at last process the unfolding pattern of events in our lives, digest them, absorb the nourishing and enrichening relevance of these whilst discarding and letting go of the painful or resentful content. This activity of the mind will lead us on to a deeper understanding of the principles upon which life-processes are based and this will make it possible for us to respond to these life-processes with new dynamism and creativity. We grow wise and joyful!

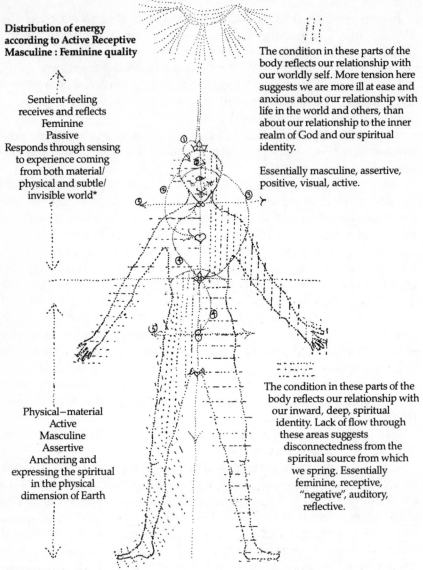

Distribution of energy according to Active Receptive Masculine : Feminine quality

Sentient-feeling
receives and reflects
Feminine
Passive
Responds through sensing
to experience coming
from both material/
physical and subtle/
invisible world*

The condition in these parts of the body reflects our relationship with our worldly self. More tension here suggests we are more ill at ease and anxious about our relationship with life in the world and others, than about our relationship to the inner realm of God and our spiritual identity.

Essentially masculine, assertive, positive, visual, active.

Physical–material
Active
Masculine
Assertive
Anchoring and
expressing the spiritual
in the physical
dimension of Earth

The condition in these parts of the body reflects our relationship with our inward, deep, spiritual identity. Lack of flow through these areas suggests disconnectedness from the spiritual source from which we spring. Essentially feminine, receptive, "negative", auditory, reflective.

* Mind and heart function as one confusion in conflict with itself until the emotions can be held still and therefore able to give a clear, ripple-free reflection of the contents of the mind. This does not happen until the mind can be held receptive to the soul and spiritual realm. When this is achieved the mind gradually learns to attune its self rhythm to that of the soul (love and light) and becomes positive to the emotional life, learning to cast upon the still waters of the emotional life the reflected image of the beauty of the spiritual plane. Think of a still, still lake or pool reflecting the wonder of the heavens.

Figure 8

This sequence of events is a cycle which repeats itself at an ever-deepening level, in rhythm with the steady dissolving away of the bands of tension. These cycles almost always follow a pattern of four. Four sessions brings relaxation and loosening, then a confrontation with these (sometimes difficult and explosive, sometimes not), and finally an integration which is usually reflected by a lull and stillness in the flow of energy through the etheric vehicle. Each cycle of four sessions will carry the patient through the journey of shedding a band of tension. Often the first cycle of four will adjust the superficial distortion of flow, whilst the next four will carry the patient through the cause of this superficial distortion. What takes place after this will become progressively more subtle and less easily defined. . . Sometimes it will take many more than eight sessions to get to grips with the root of a person's problem. This speed of tension unravelling is influenced by many things: the degree of consistent and unchanging daily stress in a person's life, the degree of fear of life, both past and future, and readiness of a person to pursue self-help approaches which energise his physical body and soothe and stimulate his spiritual life, and, very important, the extent to which a person has already in his/her life a means of self-expression such as painting, playing a musical instrument, drama.

No matter what depth of tension-band is currently being worked upon, each cycle of sessions will follow a pattern. Release at the Solar Plexus will bring a corresponding relaxation at the left brain. These two loosenings will enable both Heart and right brain to free up a bit. As Soulforce can flow more easily through the right brain, the next memory bank will be dislodged, releasing into the now slightly less tense left brain, memories of events which give significance to present ways of responding to life. If the left brain is relaxed enough, the patient will easily deal with what he is beginning to recognise. Sometimes extra work is needed at this point to help the person successfully integrate the new understandings.

Sometimes this cyclic unfoldment will get stuck and some particularly resistant knot will be visible to the healer, but not budgeable. Often the patient will find a reason to cease sessions and this is the right thing to do because obviously the time is inappropriate, in the deeper spiral of his life, for this particular knot to be unravelled, and further healing would simply cause stimulation he was unable to deal with and tension would arise from this.

Although this standard pattern of congestion which begins at the Solar Plexus will apply in a general way to each of us, the detail will be different and individual. The personal nature of our own tension-bands will be reflected both by the areas which release most strongly in sessions, and also by the nature of the material which surfaces after a session.

Thus, if our overall personal problem is strongly focussed upon the Pelvic centre we will find, once this area begins to discard its tension, that we are seeing more clearly our negative and self-trapping patterns in sexual relationships, and in the area of our career, and we will begin to find it easier to act towards changing practical circumstances that don't agree with us.

If our overall personal problem is focussed upon the Heart centre, the release of this area will bring with it a clearer awareness of feelings about acknowledging our oneness with others, both in intimate and more public relationships; it will bring us closer to understanding our anxieties about vulnerability, and if it is accompanied by good release at the Base centre (adrenals), it will enable us to turn our fear of openness towards people into courage.

Of all the centres, the Heart is the most delicate and fragile at this time, and the most easily wounded or pushed too far. No forcing or pushing must ever be exerted upon this centre; it will only result eventually in depletion and more weakness, even if it seems temporarily to bring openness.

The most difficult tension to release is that focussed at the Head centres. Mental tension seems to become crystallised and embedded, perhaps because everything to do with mind is governed by will, and will is the most powerful force in the universe. The person whose brain is seriously cross-threaded will probably not pursue healing of this kind very far because he will sense that he no longer holds ultimate control when offering himself to the hands of the healer.

Problems of mental functioning are often the result of a toxic brain condition because of an unclean bloodstream. This is a physiological brain problem and not a 'mental' one. It will adjust as the physical functioning of the patient responds to healing, in particular the working of the liver. As the liver detoxifies, cleans itself and therefore achieves greater vitality, so also will the brain become clearer, calmer, more balanced, and more positive.

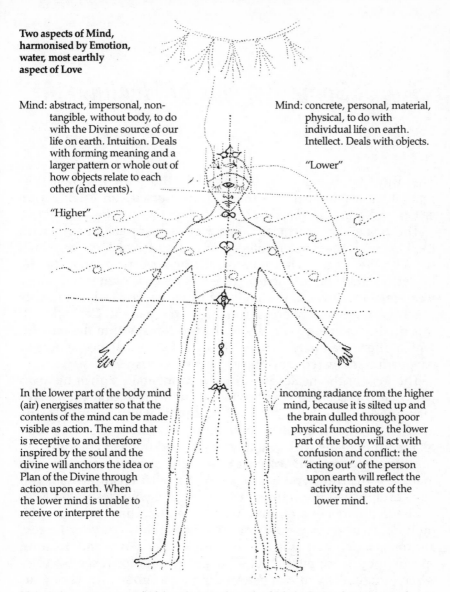

Two aspects of Mind, harmonised by Emotion, water, most earthly aspect of Love

Mind: abstract, impersonal, non-tangible, without body, to do with the Divine source of our life on earth. Intuition. Deals with forming meaning and a larger pattern or whole out of how objects relate to each other (and events).

"Higher"

Mind: concrete, personal, material, physical, to do with individual life on earth. Intellect. Deals with objects.

"Lower"

In the lower part of the body mind (air) energises matter so that the contents of the mind can be made visible as action. The mind that is receptive to and therefore inspired by the soul and the divine will anchors the idea or Plan of the Divine through action upon earth. When the lower mind is unable to receive or interpret the

incoming radiance from the higher mind, because it is silted up and the brain dulled through poor physical functioning, the lower part of the body will act with confusion and conflict: the "acting out" of the person upon earth will reflect the activity and state of the lower mind.

The whole person is a wonderful mechanism through which the Divine Spirit may work creatively in the realm of physical matter upon Earth.

Figure 9

5. Some Aspects of Healing

The aim of the healer is to stimulate the patient's own self-regulatory mechanisms so that Nature herself can establish an easier and more balanced flow of life force within that patient.

The healer has learnt to make a conscious relationship with his/her Soul, the concentrated point of spiritual force to which we all have access. This relationship makes it possible for the healer to become a carrier of energy of a higher vibratory frequency than would normally be possible. His task is to make this high frequency energy available to the patient. Contact with this quality of energy stimulates the life-force within the patient, which then gradually brings about a better balance whereby congestion is cleared, and starved areas nourished.

The task of the healer is, initially, to mentally affirm his own personal contact with the Soul; a mental projection then takes place whereby the healer sees self and patient as embraced by the Soul . . . in time you will become aware in some way of the group on the inner plane with whom you are working and you can then consciously affirm this contact also at the start of a session. The mantra with which you begin 'seals' this relationship which you have established through your thought and your desire to help.

The main area of attention until the end of the session will be the quality of energy flow you experience through your fingers and/or hands. You will be watching this flow, and relating specific point-response as you go along, to point-response elsewhere; gradually you will be building up a subtle picture of your sense of what is happening in your patient's energy. If you feel your mind is drifting too far from the subject of your work, once more check your contact with the Soul . . . repeat these re-attunements as often as you need. At first you will probably feel very self-conscious and distracted by outside noises, your physical posture, self-doubt, etc. Accept that this is inevitable when you are learning a new skill; don't be put off; reaffirm your

MEDITATION ON THE RADIATION OF LOVE

See your physical body as relaxed, at ease . . . identify the most pronounced tensions and see them slipping away until you are deeply relaxed, yet quite alert. See your emotional body as a deep, still, tranquil lake, unstirred by a single ripple.

See your mental body as a pure, clear, dawn sky, a few birds winging their way into the distance through the quiet, poised air, like your last few thoughts.

Project a line of light, a silver thread, from the top of your head, upwards, until you feel this line has reached the radiant sun of love and light which characterises the Soul for each of us.

Now see this love and light pouring through the physical, emotional and mental vehicles of the personality, like a great, joyful river flowing freely between its banks. See it purifying and cleansing the day-to-day awareness of self, with its problems and preoccupations.

Now see this sun, this radiant source of love, growing wider and wider until it merges with the suns of each person in this group, becoming then, of many units, one greater unit. See this focus of love and light encompassing and enfolding our group.

Divine love, so fill us with yourself, that we may become all love, and let us, in the power of your love within us, suffuse all beings with thoughts of love, compassion, joy and peace.

See this love which bathes us here extended outwards to include the whole of our area and all creatures and living beings therein . . . the whole of our country . . . oppressed people thoughout the world . . . the whole of humanity . . . the whole planet, mineral, vegetable, animal and human . . . and beyond.

Bring your attention back to this place . . . and to this group . . . hold now one person about whom you have strong feelings in the centre of this pool of lovingness that we have focussed. Identify once more with your own personal Soul, linked to you by the shining thread, the antakharana.

Step down further into your mental body or mind; feel yourself once more firmly on earth, yet aware of the continuing influence and presence of the Soul in your life.

Say the Great Invocation.

Link hands in the group and chant:

I am a circle, I am healing you; you are a circle, you are healing me: unite us, be as one; unite us, be as one.

(Repeat three times).

Radiation of Love

attunement and, if you feel the need, ask (pray) for guidance or teaching or strength – whatever you need. Trust your own contact with the Soul; but even more important, trust the desire of the Soul to work through you . . . you do actually find yourself in the position of healer because your own Soul has pushed and pulled, cajoled and coaxed, you into the role of acting as the mechanism through which it can reach and adjust those parts of God's creation which are far from the centre.

Relevant to this is your possible fear that you may do some- thing 'wrong'; I feel that this approach to healing is very safe, very gentle, but extremely thorough. This is because all you are doing is enabling the patient's own self-healing mechanism to get a firmer relationship with the patient; by the same token, you are simply the connecting link between the need, or deficit, (the patient), and the central supply. Once you have enabled the connection between these two to be made, the need will draw from the supply (the Soul) exactly what it needs, and exactly at the rate at which it can best absorb and use that supply.

If your patient experiences any kind of distress as part of a session, know that you are not personally responsible for this, so there is no need to feel guilty. However, you are there to give whatever nourishment, support and caring you can to help that person go through his/her own difficult times. Make a personal connection . . . think how you feel at similar times . . . comfort and counsel with as much sincerity and identification with the patient's feelings and state as you can. Let them know that you are there to accept, to understand, and to be leaned upon and listened to as much as the patient needs and other time demands allow. Be sure to suggest other therapy help if it seems relevant, e.g. diet, counselling, creative. Let them know that there are people ready and able to give support and aid while it is needed, but also seek to identify with the patient's own frame of reference, e.g. for someone who is accustomed to conventional religious counselling, it may be more relevant to encourage that person to re-approach a priest who had previously been of help, than to suggest they try a very different 'New Age' approach to counselling. Remember that the patient is always right – we seek to identify and work within that person's reality, which has absolute validity, and not to impose our personal way of thinking upon theirs. This is not to say that sometimes it is necessary to advise a slightly different approach to the one that has been followed; sometimes it is clear that a person is making their situation worse by doing certain things. But if possible it is always better to help someone to work things out for themselves, and to make their own decisions, than to tell them what you think they should be doing: your aim is to be as clear a mirror as possible, so that they can see themselves reflected back clear from you, and base their further self-exploration and growth upon that.

You will find in time that during a session insights as to your patient's situation will spring into your mind, or be displayed before you. It may be difficult at first to fully trust this. Don't worry. Put the 'revelation' out of your mind; re-attune with the Soul. If you find the same insight recurs even when you open yourself to the Soul in this way, assume that it is actually the Soul casting light into your mind . . . things you need to know now. Cross-reference the insight with the information coming to you through your fingertips, and according to the key of the Centres. If it fits, accept it as probably information you need to work with. In time you will find that your initial attunement in a session also serves to open your mind so that the Soul can cast into it that which it requires you to know at that time. The more you can hold your own personality still and quiescent, the clearer will this teaching via the Soul be. It is a skill – recognise that your own fear, doubt, excitement, all inhibit the effective mastering of that skill.

A word about openness

There is often talk of the centres being too open, and the need to 'close down'. I know this is a danger, because I experience it continually myself, and can now say that my apparent inability to close down has been the core of my problems all my life. However, I have been largely trained to work as I do through the pattern described above, and this has emphasised openness to the quality of the Soul, and the ability to allow energy to flow right through my being . . . even when I have begged for guidance in my problem of too great openness (at times it becomes very uncomfortable), I have not been taught to close down. However, I have been reminded to re-establish my contact with nature and the Earth through walking, gardening, swimming in the sea, spinning and knitting and making clothes.

And these things, and solitude in Nature, heal my Spirit, re-affirm a personal part of myself that often gets lost in the busy-ness of life. They teach me about my own needs and how to tend those needs, and to nurture my own self, and my own personal relationship with God, in distinction from my relationship with God that is to do with work, which I now see as something different.

Because of this, it is not really possible for me to teach you how to close down. I have come to the conclusion that it is not part of my work to 'close down' in the usual sense; but that is not to say that you should not do this . . . it is simply to say that it is not something I can give you. Return always to your contact with the Soul. If help does not come while you work in healing sessions, or in a group meditation (it is absolutely appropriate to ask for personal help in a group meditation), then arrange your life so you can spend a few days alone ('go up into the mountain'), put yourself somewhere where you can be very quiet and trace your path more and more deeply inward. Have faith in this process and let outward distractions fall away. Then meditate and ask to be shown how to deal with the problem of too great openness.

From a technical point of view I feel that healing is about flowing; healing is about making whole and making whole is about the fluid distribution of energy throughout; to shut down any part of the pathways of distribution of that fluid energy is to create a barrier: will the energy stop flowing or will it simply begin to create uncomfortable pressure upon the barrier that now prevents it flowing where previously it could go with ease?

These are questions to be considered.

Nevertheless, I know all too well how unpleasant is that too great feeling of openness. What is one actually too open to? I think it is the vibrations of other people that begin to be experienced as an intrusion because one has lost contact with one's own centre. So, in a practical sense the task is to regain contact with one's own centre, and to HOLD ONESELF THERE until one once more feels strong and courageous. It is obviously necessary to avoid too much input from others while re-finding one's own centre, as this contact draws one always out. So, as much as is possible in your work schedule, avoid all contact with people and spend the time revitalising your personal life-force by nourishing yourself with lots of fresh air (lots of oxygen to clear the head and enliven the nerves) and exercise; pamper yourself with irresistible salads, lavender oil baths, snacks of highest quality foods; soothe your emotions with music that you find healing; re-affirm your connection with your Soul and ask for guidance and for strength; if possible, arrange for someone to do the Great Central Release on you.

If it is not possible to avoid all contact with people, maintain only the contact that is essential, and seek, during this contact, to carry with you a sense of your connection with the Soul, and its protective and nourishing capacity TOWARDS YOU! Don't strive to give out anything that does not readily flow; remember your Soul contact and know that the person/people you are in contact with will draw silently directly from the Soul the resources they need without it affecting you – your task is simply to maintain that inner and upward contact. If possible also nurture yourself as mentioned above.

If you have absolutely no control over circumstances at the time (this seems mostly the case with me!), grin (or is it grimace?) and bear it, surrender to your destiny, knowing that the Soul chose you to work through because you are a survivor, and that Soul, having gone to all the trouble of getting you this far more or less intact, isn't going to suddenly allow you to be destroyed now . . . in other words, know that there is probably some essential learning (yawn! yawn!) that you are being prepared for and that the sooner you stop feeling hard done by and sorry for yourself and simply allow the torrent of life to surge through you, the sooner you will learn that lesson and enjoy the process. . . Nevertheless, don't neglect to give yourself as much self-nurturing as you can manage; don't try deep meditations; rather as much relaxation exercise as possible . . . use your hands on yourself also, and at the same time do some 'Soul-bathing'; it's exactly the same as sun-bathing only you do it inside in a comfortable place, imagining the Soul embracing you with its rays and seeping deeply into every cell in your body, relaxing tensions, melting away congestion, building in new life and vitality right through every tissue.

Use this also as a 'goodnight' exercise, after quickly assessing the day and its events . . . letting go of problems rather than dwelling upon them, and ask for sound and refreshing sleep and a joyful, loving attitude to the day that lies ahead.

6. The Influence of Jin Shin Do Points 1–30

a: Physical influence; b: Emotional influence; c: Mental influence.

1. a Eyes and vision; headaches; stiff neck and facial tensions.
   b Fear; mind over-preoccupied with negative emotions and distress; nervous tension in all its forms.
   c Subtle vision; understanding and mental perception; clearing of mental confusion and overactivity.

2. a Stomach; face; sinuses; colds and flu and toothache; lymphatic vitality and thyroid.
   b To aid integration of thoughts and feelings by helping to free throat area: higher creativity; to aid flow of feelings towards self.
   c By aiding the flow of feelings these points help the mind to clear and function with less tension.

3. a Breathing and lung and bronchial functioning; help to balance the 'timing' of electrical transmission at the brain level with passage of emotional impression through the chest and therefore aid mental and emotional balance.
   b By helping to free the throat centre these points help towards a more creative and spontaneous use of emotional and mental energy – they aid capacity to flow through life. Free tears and feelings.
   c Covered by a and b.

4. a Heartburn, shortness of breath; heart and lung functioning and muscular activity in chest/shoulder region; chest mucous.
   b Sadness; painful and sorrowful emotions that are inheld; release of tears; anxiety.

72

O thou who art the everlasting essence of things,
beyond space and time and yet within them;
thou who transcendest yet pervadest all things;
manifest Thyself to us,
feeling after Thee and seeking Thee in the
　　　　　shades of ignorance.
stretch forth Thy hand to help us,
who cannot without Thee come to Thee;
reveal Thyself to us who seek nothing
　　　　　beside Thee.

Figure 10

POINTS USED IN JIN SHIN DO

12 is found in the slight hollow just under the ankle bone at the outside; 9 is in the hollow just under the ankle bone at the inside. To find 10, follow the inside edge of the foot from the big toe to the boney protrusion: where the foot curves in from this bone the point is found. To find 11 start at the foot between small and fourth toe and follow straight up the foot towards the front edge of the ankle bone: half way along this line the 11 is found.

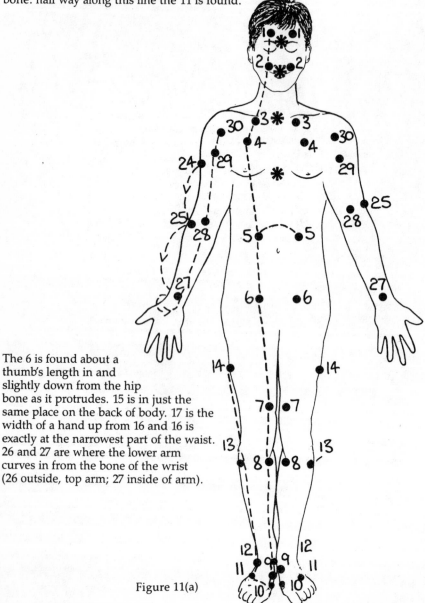

The 6 is found about a thumb's length in and slightly down from the hip bone as it protrudes. 15 is in just the same place on the back of body. 17 is the width of a hand up from 16 and 16 is exactly at the narrowest part of the waist. 26 and 27 are where the lower arm curves in from the bone of the wrist (26 outside, top arm; 27 inside of arm).

Figure 11(a)

POINTS USED IN JIN SHIN DO

• : 30 main Jin Shin Do points
★ : extra points often used

These points are acupuncture points and have
their own names and reference numbers in
acupuncture meridian lore. They are numbered
1–30 in Jin Shin Do for convenience only.

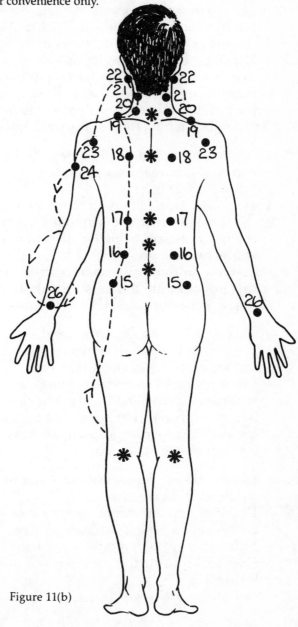

Figure 11(b)

    c Optimistic spirit, joy; capacity to love regardless of circumstances.

5. a Liver and gallbladder (right side); pancreas and stomach (left). Diaphragm and therefore breathing; abdominal tension, belching, hiccoughs, snoring; indigestion.
    b Nervous tension towards the self; insecurity; inability to act to change one's situation. Irritability and fear and tension to do with the attitudes of others towards one.
    c Tension here is directly linked with the tendency to over-react mentally; too hasty expression of mental attitudes: brittleness and negative-type mental activity; also poor mobilisation of intellect – inability to carry thought through free from fiery or fearsome emotions.

6. a Tension/relaxation of abdomen, groin, thigh and sexual organs. Menstrual cramps, lower digestive disturbances, intestinal weakness.
    b When fear is an important factor for a person, these points will become tight and without elasticity – freeing them enables a person to better carry through that which he knows he must do.
    c Carrying of thoughts out into action; respond directly to rhythm transmitted from spiritual plane to ears; organise this so it may be carried down to earth through legs.

7. a Smooth functioning of the female reproductive organs. Menstrual cramps and genital problems. Release of thighs and knees; indigestion and itching.
    b Pre-menstrual emotional tension and all tension linked with reproductive and ovarian organs.
    c Negative prison of thought linked with non-fluidity of female cyclic changes; capacity to move inner feelings out into action.

8. a Knees and legs; yin conditions; lower back pain and bodily swelling; also digestion.
    b Digestion of emotional experience; stiffness at knees always reflect poor distribution of emotional energy and poor capacity to 'process' emotional experience, i.e. to absorb its constructive elements and to eliminate its painful aspects.
    c Part of the brain which deals with processing emotional

experience: left knee relates specifically to material in the unconscious mind; right knee relates specifically to material immediately to hand and in the day-to-day or 'rational' mind.

9. a Drowsiness and excessive need to sleep; deeper and more refreshing sleep. Heels and female sexual organs; kidneys; tiredness of all limbs.
   b Sadness. Congested fear and inability to move out through feelings.
   c Capacity to fulfil one's sense of individuality in the world; creativity.

10. a Circulation; feet; balance gaps in body energy to fill deficiencies. Cold feet, cramps, abdominal and stomach tensions.
    b Nervous anxiety; hypochondria. Tension of all feelings – inhibited flow through heart centre.
    c Aids clearing of mind and proper use of mind, by easing nervous tension and insecurity.

11. a Ankles, feet, lower legs; headache, rheumatism, perspiration and excessive bodily water. Liver.
    b Ease with which all fiery and self-assertive emotions can flow.
    c Directly affects ability to mobilise self out into action and expression of individuality in life.

12. a Insomnia. Feet and knees. Headaches, hyper-tension, pain. Help release lower back. Ovaries.
    b All emotions linked with reproductive organs and throat.
    c Enable rhythm from spiritual plane to be grounded on earth according to individual expression.

13. a Muscles throughout body, including muscular soreness. Release of knees and legs. Headaches, abdominal pain and problems, constipation, lower back tension. Important to digestion.
    b Fear, extreme fright. Digestion and distribution of all emotional experience.
    c As for 8.

14. a Outer thighs, knees, legs, hip joints. Release of back points; toxicity; lower back problems and weakness of the legs.

    b Extremely important to whole nervous system and there-
fore all debilitating and shocking emotional experience,
including pain.

    c Strongly aids mind to clear through soothing and releasing
nervous system. This one is a key to release of whole
nervous system and therefore all problems throughout the
system.

15. a Bladder, hip joints, abdominal problems, constipation,
haemorrhoids, prostate and urinary problems. Freedom of
this point aids in fluidity of leg and feet movements and
therefore of the grounding and carrying through of all that
takes place further up the body.

b/c Easing according to increased capacity for carrying through
into action all emotional experience and mental intention.

16. a Kidneys, lower abdomen, lower back release; abdominal
problems, appetite balance, genital, prostate and urinary
problems. For strengthening the whole body.

    b Fear: Prime points for fear and therefore also influence
fluidity of all other emotions as fear unbalances the experience of all other emotions.

    c Clear mental functioning is greatly enhanced by releasing
fear. Awareness and integration of our fear into day-to-day
functioning enables us to use that fear as creative energy: it
can enhance our sensitivity of perception so that we can
mobilise deeper awareness of factors involved in a situation – capacity to fully participate in what is going on is
greatly enriched. The flow of adrenalin stimulated by the
fear can bring greater alertness if we can mobilise that fear!

17. a Liver (right side), pancreas (left side). Release of back and
diaphragm. Fullness in the chest, poor digestion, fainting.

    b Keys to release of solar plexus and therefore all 'negative'
personal emotion: irritability, insecurity, jealousy, anger,
impatience. Fluidity of transmission of pranic flows from
self to other, solar plexus to heart centre.

    c Release of tension of logical, rational, 'conscious' mind;
mental self-protectiveness and devices. To enhance calm
attitudes towards self.

18. a Circulation and heart; respiration and lungs; chronic problems. Upper back, shoulder, neck and arm release; difficult

breathing, coughing, hyperacidity and tiredness.

b Their condition reflects the way in which flow is happening through the heart centre: left side refers to the self and is often heavily coated and burdened with stagnant pain residues; right side refers to the other . . . both sides affect each other and tend to work antagonistically; they need to work in harmony in order for the individual to be able to experience and carry through emotional oneness. These points are extremely relevant to all our problems at this time. But be gentle: too hasty release can bring overwhelming upsurging of anguish and of tears which will be unable to flow if the throat centre is not adequately relaxed. Anxiety; broken-heartedness.

c Freeing these points enables unwinding of tight attitudes towards others but may also bring temporary mental anguish as residues of painful experience shift and clear.

19. a Resistance to 'external evils'; reducing fever; open perspiration. Shoulders, neck and arm release. Hypertension and all nervous tension.

b Another key to the nervous system and therefore to all holding on to unwanted emotions. Freeing these means better vitality and tone to use emotional energy.

c Mobilisation of humour is greatly enhanced by release of these: emotional fluctuations can be seen to dance and play their way whether good or 'bad'.

20. a Neck and shoulder tension; sex organs; headache; nervousness; tiredness; throat problems.

b Irritability and inability to cope: 'uptightness'.

c These points are the meeting-ground for the flow of emotion upwards to the mind, and the flow of thought downwards to the chest and feeling area. They reflect utterly a person's capacity to work creatively in the NOW and use thought and feeling with spontaneous, easy fluidity. This point has a strong relationship with the liver and its release will be most deep and thorough when this takes place hand-in-hand with a release of liver tensions.

21. a Key to easy flow of energy through whole body, as most of the organ meridians or their branches, flow through this narrow region. Neck, shoulder, arm, throat, voice and headaches.

b/c   Creativity: an individual's capacity to express and carry through the deeper meanings he learns through his experience in life depend upon these points.

22. a Entire body; eyes, ears, nose, mouth and brain. Neck and head tensions; colds, flu, dizziness, headaches, insomnia, nerves.
    b Emotional tensions are softened through the release of these points because of their effect upon consciousness:
    c they unlock the 'cage' of the mind and thereby free consciousness.

23. a Shoulder, scapula, neck, hypertension and high blood pressure.
    b Release contained emotional tension but rarely invoke tears.
    c Brain arhythmicity is balanced because heart rhythms are balanced by this point.

24. a Arms, shoulders and facilitate release of neck; large intestines, throat and teeth.
    b All arm release helps soothe, steady and balance emotions.
    c Because emotions are balanced, mind can also become steadier and more relaxed.

25. a Arms and elbows; stimulate production of antibodies. Fever, hypertension, constipation, skin problems.
    b Depression: knees and elbows reflect digestion of feelings and thoughts; arms in particular relate to feelings, so this point helps to shift undigested emotions.
    c Mind is aided through easing of emotions.

26. a Arms, elbows, wrists and fingers; colds, flu, headaches, rheumatism.
    b Fear: capacity of feelings to keep moving and therefore changing; aids release of heart and anxiety.
    c As for 25.

27. a Pain; arms, elbows; difficult breathing, dizziness and nausea.
    b Reflect feelings to do with love in sexuality.
    c Release of this one is very calming to mind and heart: hyperactivity through very sensitive and creative involvement in life.

28. a Arms, elbows, shoulders; cardiac and lung problems; dryness in mouth, thirst and vomiting.
    b Aids processing of emotional experience.
    c Eases mind through above.

29. a Inside of arms, release of upper back. Lung problems, fear of cold and wind.
    b Fear and palpitations from fear; when these free you know that the heart centre is expanding into mellowness.
    c Lighter-hearted humour through relaxing of heart centre.

30. a Lungs, help to free breathing and to release chest and shoulders; coughing, skin and tonsil problems.
    b Grief, oppression, all holding onto emotions: freeing these will often bring a surging of tears – release of throat centre is aided therefore also.
    c A relaxed and optimistic spirit finds space when these free.

POINTS OF PARTICULAR IMPORTANCE:
1, 10, 14, 16, 20, 22

These are key points. The way in which they relate to other points will express the overall freeing of an individual from his etheric congestion.

16 gives a clear sense of the state of the kidneys, distribution of fluid (i.e. emotional energy) throughout the system, and ease of production of adrenalin. Everything hinges upon what is happening here!

1, 14 and 22 are all about the nervous system. An individual's state of health depends on the vitality of his nervous system. For most people, the nervous system is exhausted and in need of deep rest; some people have overvitalised nervous systems but are unable to use this energy in a co-ordinated way and so become depleted as it is locked up within their own system, thus creating a kind of auto-intoxication. Freeing these points is about helping a person to 'go with the flow' more easily and live in tune with his/her inner cyclic rhythms. These are the keys to at-one-ment.

10 is about physical, emotional and mental distribution of energy: our general lack of balance means that some areas get too much energy whereas others get little or even none; this point

enables those lacking to receive what they need, and for those with too much, to be drained.

20 is the lock, 1, 14 and 22 the keys; the one is useless without the other, yet all rely upon the hinge – 16!

Until this point (20) is released, real harmony with the ebb and flow of our cosmic or soul-self is inaccessible, for that soul-self is unable to pour through our feelings (heart and solar plexus) and our body and out into joyous expression on Earth. . . Oneness, Divine Unity, requires to manifest itself through the diversity and richness of individual bodies; for us now, on the individual planet Earth . . . it is the goal of our lives to make visible that Oneness through bringing body and personality into harmony with Soul.

7. Jin Shin Do Release Patterns

INTRODUCTION

It is possible when necessary to work with your patient in almost any position: on the floor, on a bed or on a chair. But it is much better for you, if you are able to stand with your spine quite straight, and your feet firmly on the ground, for the duration of the session. Your patient can achieve the deepest relaxation when lying flat on their back, and your nervous system is able to transmit and ground the high frequency energy with which it is working, with the least amount of strain. A high massage bench or table, with a couple of inches of foam covering, is the best thing to use.

Some of the points you will work with will be far away from each other, especially if you are short and your patient is tall. In this case, draw up the knees of your patient before you begin the 'movement' of points involving the stretch, so you will be able to reach without losing your upright position. Always begin and end each session with the mantras given and the closing sequence of points, and take plenty of time at the very beginning of the session to align yourself with the Soul before projecting this alignment to include your patient.

Use either the fingertips of the three middle fingers of each hand, or your palms, depending on which feels most sensitive to you. Cover the general area of the point and know that in time you will intuitively sense exactly where the greatest point of tension-holding is. Use your hands a few inches away from the body, although when you first begin you may want to touch the body lightly just to locate the point you are working with better. In time, your sensitivity will result in you using your hands closer to the body with some people, but further away with others. This will be in response to the needs of the layers of congestion in the etheric vehicle of your patient, and as your hands grow more sensitive to this.

When using back points, you will naturally have more body contact but can still press your hands away from the body, in order to minimise this. Body contact will tend to dull the response in the etheric vehicle.

Always shake each hand loosely after it leaves each point, and away from your patient's body. If you do not do this you will tend to collect uncomfortable static electricity build-up in your hands which will adversely affect your own etheric body.

Also, always put your hands in water immediately you have completed a session.

These two disciplines help maintain 'spiritual hygiene', and make it easier for you to re-centre and focus your own etheric vehicle with your personal consciousness. It is dangerous to the integrity of the self to allow yourself to remain too diffused in the etheric field, and detached from your own personal identity, for too long.

It is also a good idea, for the same reasons, to spend a few moments after your patient has left, before you start to work with someone else, and at the end of the day, drawing your consciousness carefully back into yourself (watch your breathing and scan your spine), aligning it once more with the Soul, and seeing yourself in the centre of a Cross of Love and Light connecting the Soul with the Earth. This is a very useful image to work with and has very concrete powers of protection for the healer.

When you use your hands in these tension-release patterns, you are playing the most wonderful musical instrument ever made: the human body . . . your hands touch the notes, with tenderness and sensitivity to the sounds they emit; whilst your mind listens to the sound arising, and seeks to harmonise this with the sound that is simultaneously issuing from the Soul, (which in turn seeks to produce a perfectly pitched chord as it passes through the human instrument).

You are a musician in the orchestra of life, seeking to participate in the wonder and mystery of its eternal music! I wish you great joy in this experience.

BEGIN AND END EACH SESSION AS FOLLOWS:

With hands to either side of the patient's head (an inch or two outside of the ears), make your alignment with the Soul; use the image of the thread of light running between the ground, through yourself, and up to the Soul; affirm that it is the Soul end of this channel of communication which is in control; feel that the presence of the Soul encompasses your personal presence. See this presence now moving out to encompass and include the presence of the person with whom you are working. Let your awareness of this person's outer, dense self drift away to be replaced instead by a sense of their subtle or etheric presence:

With purity of motive, inspired by a loving heart, we offer ourselves for this work of healing. This offer we make as a group, and to the one we seek to heal.

Whatever release pattern you have used, you have opened up a channel for an increased flow of force; it is important to re-centre your patient after this in order to aid him in any adjustment that may be necessary after such an opening:

R hand covers Crown; L hand (or fingertips) at base of skull.
R hand remains here; L hand moves to heart centre (at front); L hand moves to Third Eye centre.

Draw your own presence back slightly from your patient and raise hands to your own Heart centre, palms facing outwards:

May the Love of the one Soul, focussed in this group, radiate upon you, my brother, and permeate every part of your being, healing, soothing and strengthening, and dissipating all that hinders service and good health.

While these beginning and closing mantras are being thought, be aware of your contact with the Soul: you are dedicating yourself with sincerity to the purpose of the Soul for the duration of the healing within the mantras.

Please remember to shake your hands away from your patient each time each hand moves from one point to the next. Always put your hands into water as·soon as you finish a healing session. This is really very important.

THE NECK RELEASE

This releases the neck/shoulder/head area and can be used alone to calm someone who is in the throes of mental hyperactivity or emotional distress; it, or an extended version, is also used to end a full session and to release tension that may have accumulated in this area after release lower down the body.

NECK RELEASE

Stand at the head of the patient:

LH – l23
RH – r23
LH – l19
RH – r19
LH – l20
RH – r20
LH – l21
RH – r21
LH – l22
RH – r22

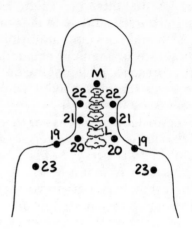

EXTENDED NECK RELEASE

LH – l23	LH – l21
RH – M	RH – C
RH – r23	RH – r21
LH – M	LH – C
LH – l19	LH – l22
RH – B	RH – r1
RH – r19	RH – r22
LH – B	LH – l1
LH – l20	
RH – A	
RH – r20	
LH – A	

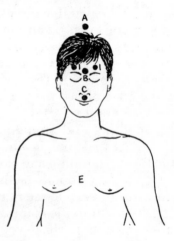

RH = right hand. LH = left hand. l = left side. r = right side.

Always use the neck release, or the extended neck release, at the end of every session, short or long. This is very important as tensions released further down the body will tend to result in a loosening of congestion at the head and neck area. This loosening will cause the patient discomfort if it is not smoothed away and freed by the neck release. Also, complete each session, after the neck release and before the closing prayer, with the final balancing step:

{ RH – A
{ LH – M   Draw back from the head of the patient, bring your
  LH – E   hands to your own heart centre, palms outwards and
  LH – B   think the words of the closing prayer.

Figure 12

The basic neck release allows tension of a superficial nature to be eased and freed from the neck and head area. The extended version deepens and carries further this release and can therefore be deeply opening.

This may be positive and even necessary for some people, whereas it may leave others too exposed and vulnerable too quickly: consider the 'feel' of that person in relationship with the action of the points you will be working upon.

23s: help to release the Heart centre, so influence all holding of emotion; also particularly related to intimate relationships; they free the lungs, and high blood pressure and bronchial trouble. Linked with A they do all this, but deepen conscious awareness of tension as A influences central brain processes strongly.

19s: uptightness, worry, nervous system, weariness, hyperactivity. With the Third Eye centre they do all this but directly linked to pituitary gland functioning (governing all the other glands and consciousness).

20s: frustration – energy which is not flowing; the reproductive system and its problems; irritability and uptightness – extremely key point for relaxing self-image. When linked to the Crown centre: helps the relationship with the Divine and the environment.

21s: creativity and it is usually tense or stuck. When linked to C it deeply releases the carotid gland, the sinuses, and the inner brain processes.

22s: help mental activity to integrate with the emotions; they strongly relax consciousness and a 'tight head'. Linked with 1s, this influence on consciousness is deepened and balance is aided between the two sides of the brain. The 1s also influence the eyes.

THE GREAT CENTRAL RELEASE

The Great Central release will begin to remove obstructions in the flow of energy through the central channels, thus enabling a person to draw his attention in from the periphery of his being and to hold it poised, balanced and aligned and in better relationship with the Soul. Too much distracting activity, focussing upon outer conditions, upon the advice, views or behaviour of others, or worry about one's outgoing relationships, blocks the fluid intake of Soul contact and its distribution. We become

GREAT CENTRAL RELEASE

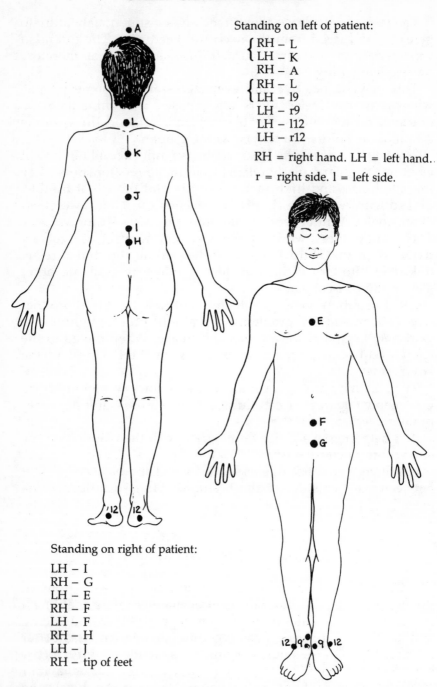

Standing on left of patient:

$\left\{ \begin{array}{l} \text{RH} - \text{L} \\ \text{LH} - \text{K} \end{array} \right.$

RH – A

$\left\{ \begin{array}{l} \text{RH} - \text{L} \\ \text{LH} - \text{l9} \end{array} \right.$

LH – r9

LH – l12

LH – r12

RH = right hand. LH = left hand.

r = right side. l = left side.

Standing on right of patient:

LH – I
RH – G
LH – E
RH – F
LH – F
RH – H
LH – J
RH – tip of feet

Figure 13

scattered, feel a victim of people or circumstances, and out of control.

By loosening the tightness in the central channels for energy distribution the patient becomes able to draw in and concentrate his life force at the core of his being and also to make fresh contact with his inner spiritual source, Soul, or true healer. This release has an immediately psycho-emotional soothing and calming effect and is of great value to anyone emotionally or psychically distraught.

Linking L and K begins to relax the throat centre so that emotional tension at the Heart centre may find expression, or flow; moving to A deepens this by relaxing the Crown centre, thereby making possible a more integrated use of spiritual force. Linking L with 9s and 12s at the ankles draws energy from the throat through the pelvis and legs, releasing the pelvis for better outward expression in the physical dimension of creative energy between the throat and the pelvis. So this phase has worked primarily upon the areas for the expression through the individual of the Divine Life.

The second phase emphasises the midriff and the Base centre – the individual will to allow the Divine Life through, which so often becomes tense and rigid with fear: I with G draws energy from the kidneys through the base of the spine; G with E balances and soothes the Base and the Heart (calming emotional unsteadiness); E with F continues this. Then F to H very deeply calms and loosens nervous fear, and deeper fear; H with J carries this through to the Solar Plexus in a penetrative way and linking J with the tip of the feet draws the energy that can now flow through the midriff, physical creative area and Base centre, down into the feet where it can be anchored: the individual is able to pick up his bag of troubles and march on through life, after feeling rooted to the spot with fear and confusion!

APPLICATION OF THE REGULATOR AND BRIDGE RELEASES

The Regulator, along with the Bridge, is the release which works to bring about a balance in the flow of inner energy, so that a person may continue his work of exploration of his self, or personal life, and of the other, and the Divine Life, access to which we all share.

THE REGULATOR RELEASE

Stand on the left to begin:

A { RH – l21
    LH – r1
    LH – r4
    LH – r5
    LH – r6
    LH – l8
    LH – l10

B { RH – l19
    LH – l11
    LH – l13
    LH – l14
    RH – l20
    RH – l22

C { RH – l23
    LH – l24
    LH – l26
    LH – l27

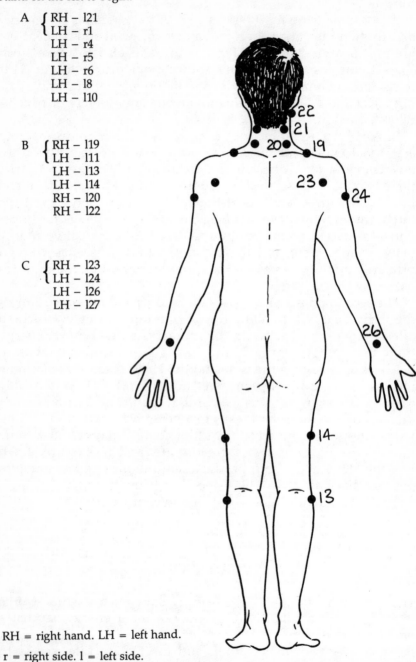

RH = right hand. LH = left hand.

r = right side. l = left side.

Figure 14(a)

THE REGULATOR RELEASE

Repeat on right side:

A { LH – r21
    RH – l1
    RH – l4
    RH – l5
    RH – l6
    RH – r8
    RH – r10

B { LH – r19
    RH – r11
    RH – r13
    RH – r14
    LH – r20
    LH – r22

C { LH – r23
    RH – r24
    RH – r26
    RH – r27

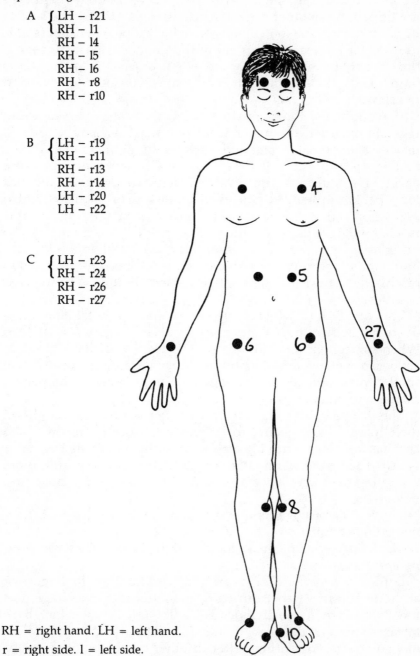

RH = right hand. LH = left hand.
r = right side. l = left side.

Figure 14(b)

The Regulator is used when the scales of a person's energy are tipped too much in one direction; the Bridge is used when they are tipped in the other direction. The Regulator could be said to be good when a person is too YANG; the Bridge when a person is too YIN. Each release brings about the same needed balance, but the one will be more appropriate when someone is too tight, too hard, too quick; the other when a person is too loose, too soft and too slow.

If in doubt, use the Regulator . . . it is very safe . . . its task is to regulate disorder, no matter what that disorder may be. It will usually bring greater calm and clarity of thought, a more relaxed and lighthearted attitude to current conflict, without stimulating a surfacing of deeply imprisoned tensions which may be difficult for a person to handle. However, its task is to 'regulate' and if regulation at that time requires the surfacing of old cobwebs, this is what will take place. On the whole, the Bridge is more likely to bring about a deeper stimulation: it works mainly upon the YIN, or inner and receptive part of one's makeup and so is designed to reach down into our deepest and most hidden or protected recesses.

Use the Bridge when someone is flooded with emotion – overwhelmed by hurt feelings or a sense of weakness or fear. When someone is rooted to the spot by fear, or unable to think or act because of a depth of emotion on the surface, this release will soothe this state, get the feelings flowing, and leave the person calmer and more centred.

The Bridge is for someone whose inner self has got caught on the outside; the Regulator for one who is stuck in his outer self and has lost touch with his feelings. On the whole the Regulator is called for more frequently. The Bridge requires a little more discretion as it may leave a person feeling a little too open and vulnerable.

The Regulator governs the liver and the mind: fire, assertiveness and the spirit.

The Bridge governs the kidneys and the heart: water, receptivity and the earth.

Both releases are called for in colds and flu. Use the Regulator at the beginning, either during or just after the fever stage; use the Bridge when much mucous is flowing or catarrhal. Both releases strongly free neck, shoulders and head and so help to get mental energy circulating better through the torso and down to earth.

Use the Regulator for strong digestive discomfort from poor liver secretions and stomach tone – someone who eats with impatience and gets headaches and stomach pain after eating.

Someone who is mentally tense, uptight, critical, over-analytical, needs the Regulator; discomfort in the legs is another symptom.

Use the Bridge for heart and chest discomfort, menstrual difficulties, blocked nose and catarrh, pains in the arms and back, weak kidneys and poor distribution of fluid; also someone who feels they cannot use their mind (. . . when this is simply because their feelings are blurring their thought). The Bridge is particularly good for allergic people.

It will seem very confusing at first to distinguish the two applications. As you develop a sense of the relationship between liver and kidneys, assertive and receptive, Spirit and Earth, you will feel easier with your choice of which to use – trust your intuition when in an alignment with the Soul and if in doubt use the Regulator.

In using these releases, sense the way in which the two hands relate to each other: one hand will always be staying at one point while the other hand moves through a sequence of points. The steady hand provides the rhythm whilst the mobile hand provides the melody. You are the instrument through which the Divine Musician seeks to work out his song; the more perfectly you can tune your mind to the vibration and radiation of the Soul, the more readily can that song be perfected.

The hand that holds the base, rhythm or steady point will produce the deepest release: base your interpretation of inner unblocking upon what you sense happening here.

These are simply notes, a guide to begin from: you will learn the most by applying these releases and listening to the message of your hands and the Soul while you work.

THE BELT AND PENETRATING RELEASE
THE CLEAR THINKING RELEASE

Although these two release patterns each have their own individual usefulness and can be used alone with great value, it will make understanding the deeper to study them together. We'll consider them one at a time first and then as a pair.

THE BRIDGE RELEASE

Stand on the left to begin:

A { RH – l22
    { LH – r2
      LH – r3
      LH – r4
      LH – r outside top pubic bone
      LH – l9

B { RH – l16
    { LH – l little toe tip
      LH – l12
      LH – l15

C { RH – l23
    { LH – l17
      LH – l18
      LH – l middle finger
      LH – l2

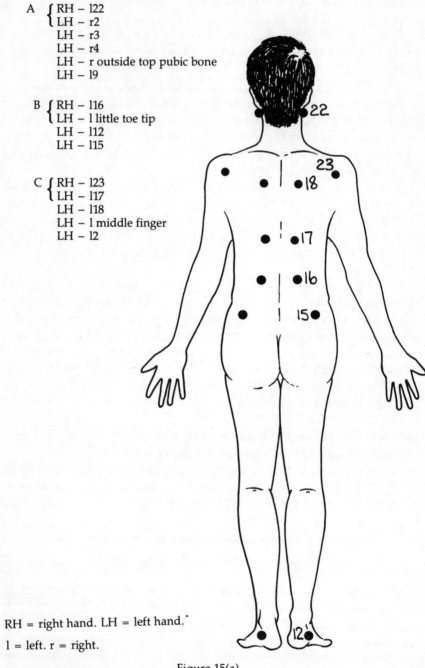

RH = right hand. LH = left hand.

l = left. r = right.

Figure 15(a)

THE BRIDGE RELEASE

Repeat on right side:

A { LH – r22
    RH – l2
    RH – l3
    RH – l4
    RH – l outside pubic bone
    RH – r9

B { LH – r16
    RH – r little toe
    RH – r12
    RH – r15

C { LH – r23
    RH – r17
    RH – r18
    RH – r middle finger
    RH – r2

RH = right hand. LH = left hand.

r = right side. l = left side.

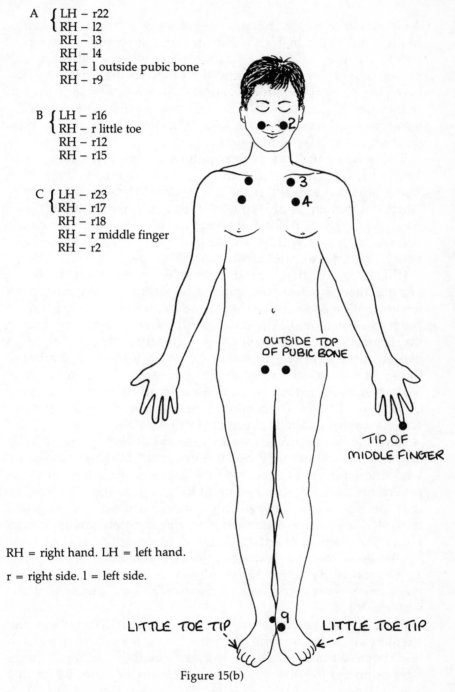

Figure 15(b)

THE BELT AND PENETRATING RELEASE

As its name suggests, this pattern works in a deep and penetrating way upon the belt, or waist and lumbar region. Its two base points are the 16 and the 6, each close together at waist and pelvis, one at the back (16) and the other on the front (6) of the body. All the other points used are on the legs except for two points (26, 27) at the wrists. So tensions are drawn through the legs to free the whole pelvic area, from the lumbar region right through to the base of the spine.

The pelvis is the foundation upon which the whole body rests. Yet for most people it is dull and stiff with accumulated tensions. These tensions will influence the flexibility and creativity with which the patient is able to deal with his career, home life, and physical exercise. All the material conditions upon which his survival depends will be affected by the clarity and ease with which energy is able to pass through this area.

Circulation of all kinds (etheric but also more 'gross' or dense, i.e. the bloodstream) through the legs will be constrained by tensions allowed to remain here. The condition of energy flow in the legs reflects and influences the condition of energy flow in the brain. Therefore, freeing the circulation through the legs makes possible a freer movement of energy through the brain; thoughts will be clearer, memories more accessible and therefore more readily 'digested' (i.e. the useful part of memories, which contributes to growth, absorbed, and the less relevant or constructive painful details eliminated or let go of).

This release pattern is, therefore, an aid to freeing up the brain for someone who is very clouded or dulled in their minds, and who finds it difficult to connect the different aspects of their life experience into a dynamic point of focussed energy. This implies that their progress through into their future lacks vitality and control: they will mostly feel a victim of their circumstances rather than a creative artist in the unfoldment of their life.

The word 'creative' is doubly relevant here because the pelvic area contains the Pelvic centre, which works hand in hand with the Throat centre to circulate creative energy throughout the system.

Freeing the Pelvis, then, as well as stimulating a better circulation of energy through the lower torso and legs, and therefore the brain, also helps to make possible a stronger, easier flow of energy through the physical creative centre. By freeing

BELT AND PENETRATING RELEASE

Starting on the left side:

1 { RH – l16   16 is base
  { LH – l11
    LH – l26

2 { RH – l6   6 is base
  { LH – l7
    LH – l8
    LH – l10
    RH – l27

Arrows indicate that the point is out of the main picture – on back or side of body. Check with chart showing all Jin Shin Do points.

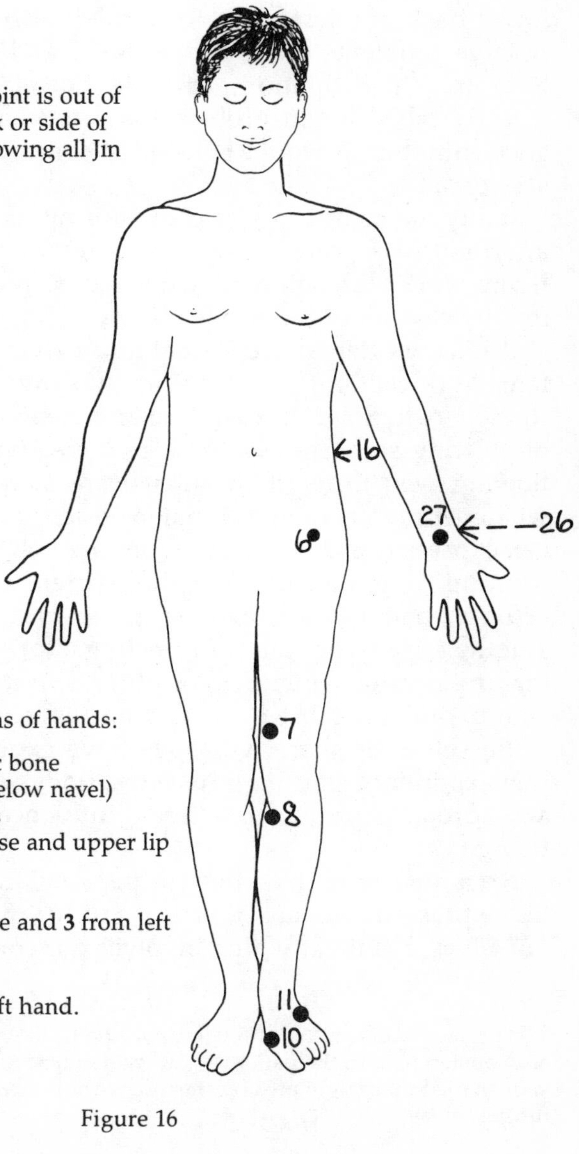

And to complete left side:
work as follows using palms of hands:

3 { LH – top of pubic bone
  { RH – hara (just below navel)
    RH – solar plexus
    RH – between nose and upper lip
    RH – third eye

Repeat 1 and 2 on right side and 3 from left side once more.

RH = right hand. LH = left hand.

r = right side. l = left side.

Figure 16

this lower creative centre the Throat centre is also helped to release.

The Belt and Penetrating release will be called for when you wish to loosen stuckness at the head in a not too intense or direct way,* when you want to deepen your release of the Throat centre, and when you want to work on physical problems in the lower back, pelvis and legs.

It is a good place to begin where back problems, especially lower back problems, are concerned; also menstrual and reproductive problems (men and women) and lower digestive problems (e.g. constipation, irritable bowel syndrome). It is not directly called for in problems where there is hormonal imbalance, although it would be used at some stage during a series of sessions.

If anyone comes to you complaining of conflict in their home and/or at work, or with sexual frustrations, think of this release; if you work with someone who cannot freely exercise their body for any reason, think of this release.

It is very often at the Throat and Pelvic centres that the worst tangled thicket of tension occurs. It is my feeling that congestion in the Heart, Solar Plexus, Base and Head centres occurs because of existing stuckness at these two creative centres. If energy is flowing well through these two areas, we are able to express whatever mental or emotional experience we are shocked by; we can express this downwards from the Pelvis through the legs, by running, jumping, digging the garden, or other very physical activity, and we can express it upwards from the Throat by singing, speaking out our feelings, praying, writing poetry, making music or pictures, or other activity which gives expression to our spirit. If we have no means to express, or put outside of ourselves or share, what we have experienced, the shock of that experience stays in our system, lodged as fear in the kidneys and adrenal cortex, from where it influences all other parts of our being.

No matter how shocking our personal trauma may be, if it can be expressed we are able to put it into a context beyond ourselves, a context which involves our condition as shared with

---

* Sometimes working too directly upon the head can stimulate resistance and also tension pain in the patient . . . it is often best to coax tensions away from a very snarled up or tight area by starting with the area which corresponds but is furthest away.

all other life, and so which involves oneness, and therefore leads us towards a deeper understanding of the processes of life. The deeper our understanding of the processes of life, the richer our experience of that life can be, even if we continue to be exposed to trauma.

The beginning base point of the Belt and Penetrating is the 16. This is the major Jin Shin Do point which affects the kidneys. Therefore it strongly affects the state of fear in a person. It is fear locked into the kidney area (the lumbar region: the waist, immediately above the hips) which primarily causes stagnation in the pelvis. If this congestion of fear builds up we will be increasingly 'rooted to the spot', and unable to move through or out of the situation causing the fear; the foundation, or root of our earthly beings, the pelvic square, will be stuck and immobile; the fear will spread to all parts of our being, and frustration will steadily become a constant companion. There are two common responses to frustration: one is to explode volcanically when the frustration becomes unbearable; the other is to steadily develop a numbness and lack of response to oneself, and therefore in time also to others.

THE CLEAR THINKING RELEASE

The three 'movements' of this release are based upon 22, 21 and 19. So it is a release which unravels the Throat centre. In the first two movements the other points used are far away at the legs, feet and ankles, and so the dynamics of the hand links made are 'long and thin'; in the last movement they are 'short and thick', or intense, involving arm and head points. Using the 22, the other hand works up the outside of the opposite leg, bringing a light soothing of mental clutteredness. Using the 21, major point influencing creativity in the whole body, the other hand works at the opposite ankle, through which Throat and Pelvic blocked creativity is adjusted. Using the 19, the other hand works on the arm on the same side, and the base moves to 20 and then 22, so that thoughts focussed in emotional turmoil can be stilled and we can see more clearly through the fog of upset feelings.

So this is very much a release which enables a mind clouded with the results of disturbed emotions to become clear and ordered once more. This makes it possible to stand back from the emotional factors and to assess with greater detachment the

CLEAR THINKING RELEASE

Start on left side:

1 { RH – l22   base is 22
  { LH – r11
    LH – r13
    LH – r14

2 { RH – l21   base is 21
  { LH – r9
    LH – r12

3 { RH – l19   base is 19, 20, 22
  { LH – l24
    RH – l20
    LH – l26
    LH – r1
    RH – l22

RH = right hand. LH = left hand.

r = right side. l = left side.

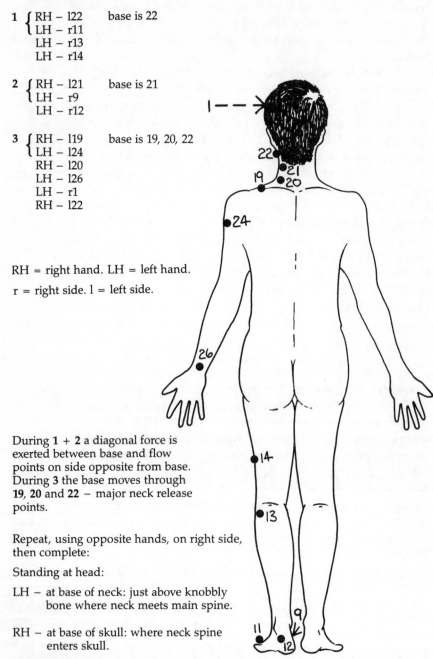

During **1 + 2** a diagonal force is
exerted between base and flow
points on side opposite from base.
During **3** the base moves through
19, 20 and **22** – major neck release
points.

Repeat, using opposite hands, on right side,
then complete:

Standing at head:

LH – at base of neck: just above knobbly
      bone where neck meets main spine.

RH – at base of skull: where neck spine
      enters skull.

Figure 17

elements at work; being able to do this in turn makes it possible to draw conclusions and to come to decisions, also knowing why one has come to those decisions.

This release has such an effect partly because it is based upon neck points. Freeing the neck in this way has two main results: it enables the traffic jam which habitually builds up at the throat, simply because it is so tightly-packed with nerves, to clear, so that information can once again get from the brain to the main part of the body; but also it enables thoughts to flow from Head to Heart and the feelings that reside there, so making it possible for thoughts and feelings to become integrated or at-oned; this in turn makes it possible for us to become centred once again, from our dis-coordinated or scattered previous state.

When centred it is safe to act; when scattered we are unsure where our actions are coming from and so we suffer insecurity and uncertainty.

The Clear Thinking can be used where any emotional or mental turmoil exists, but particularly where a patient is faced with decisions he or she feels too confused to make. If used where a scattered state is mostly emotional, it will have a soothing effect, but other release patterns (e.g. Great Central, Bridge) would have a more profound effect.

It is used with great benefit when a first series of sessions is completed and the patient has freed himself from outer emotional turmoil, yet still experiences a fogginess or dulledness in the mind. The Clear will gently begin to soften taut knots underlying this fogginess, without too suddenly or forcefully releasing head tensions: deep-seated head tensions can be linked with painful memories which have fallen deep into the unconscious mind. To stir such memories up to the surface, where they are seen and recognised, should not be done too quickly. They are inevitably painful and the patient may not yet be emotionally resilient enough to readily confront these and the realisation of the impact they have had upon the whole life.

At all times work with gentleness – coax away surface tensions. Even if you can see what lies beneath these let that emerge in its own time. If in doubt do release patterns which you know will soothe and nourish rather than penetrate to the deeper recesses of old scars. The Clear Thinking and the Belt and Penetrating are both gentle, soothing patterns.

USED AS A PAIR

The Belt and Penetrating is used first, in order to draw tensions away from the head; the Clear comes next, to deepen the loosening at the Throat centre which the pelvic clearing will have begun, and to deepen the soothing and clearing at the brain. Finally, the Neck Release removes tensions which have been loosened and gathered at the throat area during the first two releases: it re-centres the brain after the relative disorientation that the adjustment will have brought. Any adjustment brings a subtle, inner change and therefore disorientation – sometimes our tensions protect as well as imprison us.

This sequence of three release patterns is wonderful to carry deeper any freeing that has taken place through the creative centres: the Pelvis and the Throat. It would not usually be used to begin a first series of sessions, but is a good follow- up to either the Regulator or Bridge, and is often a good place to begin a second series of four sessions.

If a first series was about releasing superficial emotional congestion around the Solar Plexus (this is often the case), this combination can quickly carry a patient into a much deeper ability to express and more creatively direct locked-up and frustrated energy. By working gently but effectively upon the Pelvic and Throat centres it makes possible a more rapid draining away through these two regions of stifled and congested force. A patient will often quickly begin to take control of his/her life circumstances when this combination is used to initiate a second series of sessions in this way. Taking control like this will bring a stronger sense of positivity about the healing work being done because the patient will experience, perhaps for the first time ever, the sense of knowing his own strengths, and being able to direct and activate those strengths: the patient will begin to experience true creativity which is really the capacity to work consciously with the universal forces which at root govern all our life-processes.

It is not appropriate to use this pair where there is excess surface emotional turbulence; this calls for the Great Central and the Clear. The Belt and Penetrating combined with the Clear Thinking is a bland sequence, called for when the etheric vehicle is quite calm and lulled, at rest between episodes of throwing out dross; used at such a time it can gently ease more tightness from the Pelvis and Throat, thereby making possible a route whereby

USES OF THE BELT AND PENETRATING RELEASE

6 More active throat and pelvic centres means better capacity to express self and therefore to act out life meaning.

4 Tensions drawn away from head makes for clearer thoughts, surer sense of direction: the feet which can begin to move again also have somewhere to go…

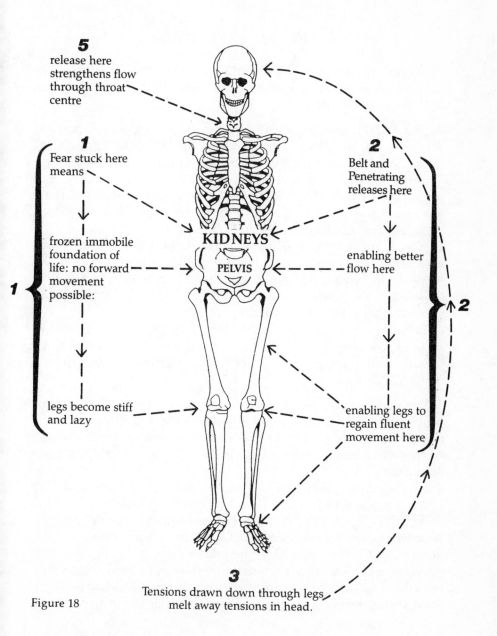

5 release here strengthens flow through throat centre

1 Fear stuck here means

2 Belt and Penetrating releases here

frozen immobile foundation of life: no forward movement possible:

1

legs become stiff and lazy

KIDNEYS

PELVIS

enabling better flow here

2

enabling legs to regain fluent movement here

3 Tensions drawn down through legs melt away tensions in head.

Figure 18

deeper tensions lodged at emotional and mental centres can surface and be eased away from the person. It is a pair of releases to be used when the nervous system is still and strong, to make possible a yet more profound relaxation at all levels of the patient.

THE BACK RELEASE

The Back release has a threefold effect: it deeply relaxes the nervous system, frees up the brain and thinking faculty, and adjusts back disorder.

a. The Back release acts directly, and in a deep way, upon the spine. By enabling energy to flow more easily through the spine it allows messages from the brain to reach the organs, muscles and soft tissue of the body more quickly and smoothly. This means that the body is able to respond more readily and alertly to any stimuli reaching it from the environment. The result of this is that:

b. The nervous system is more relaxed and at ease . . . the Back release has a great capacity to unravel knots and tangles in the nervous system and so it can help a person to relax in a steadily deepening way, and thereby cope with stresses and strains with less fuss and jarred nerves.

c. Because it makes possible an easier flow of messages through the spine it also will leave the brain better able to see through any confusion: it will soothe and strengthen the mental faculty.

The Back release also has a wonderful capacity to aid all back problems, whether they are at the pelvis, the Solar Plexus centre, the Heart centre or the Throat centre. Many problems in the day-to-day life will simply melt away if tensions in the Back are adjusted.

It is a release which has a more direct influence upon the nervous system and the mind, rather than the emotions, and yet emotional congestion can flow more quickly away after it because the mind is cleared (and therefore able to let go), and the nerves soothed. Whilst the Regulator affects the mind and nervous system by freeing tension at the liver, the Back does so by releasing taut nerves in the spine. It would not usually be used at the start of a sequence of sessions, although this can be appropriate if the patient complains specifically of back pain, or is excessively nervous.

It is an excellent way to deepen, in an easy way, the level of relaxation possible when someone is moving from one cycle of release into a deeper cycle. But it would not usually be used to soothe rough edges after a patient has experienced a period of emotional clearing, and the inner anguish which can go with this. The Regulator or Belt and Penetrating or Great Central are much more appropriate for this kind of soothing of rough edges. This is because they work closer to the periphery of the patient, whilst the Back reaches a more intense depth, and does have the power to free deep blocks. It has the potential, because of this, to draw deep problems up to the surface where they can be dealt with, but where they may also cause some temporary distress.

The Back release is most frequently used where back trouble is a constant problem, and when you wish to bring about a deeper level of relaxation to the central nervous system.

The first movement uses the 15 as its base point, moving with the other hand, through the length of the leg, down the under and outside and up the topside. This is similar to the movement of the Belt and Penetrating and has the same effect of clearing congestion at the Pelvic centre by drawing tensions down through the legs and in this way allowing the brain to be freed of clutter.

The second movement has the 21 as its base, whilst the other hand works up the underside of the back to the 18, at which stage this becomes the base and the other hand crosses over to the inside of the wrist. This movement is completed by linking the topside of the wrist with the 19. So this movement deeply emphasises the areas of the body which store emotional pain. Yet because its effect is so directly upon the spine, and because the whole release is so soothing to the brain, it is unusual for it to result in a lot of painful turmoil too close to the surface of the patient, although it does have the potential for this effect.

Comparing the Back release with the Bridge is interesting in this context. I think the Bridge should be used more rarely and with greater care than the Back and this is really because the Back, although having the power to ease emotional congestion, is really a mental or masculine or assertive release. It puts a person in contact with their self-assertiveness, helps the patient to feel more at ease with this aspect of himself, whilst the Bridge puts the person in contact with their receptivity, their femininity,

BACK RELEASE

Starting on the left side:

1 { RH – 115
  { LH – l behind knee
  LH – 112
  LH – little toe
  LH – l6

2 { RH – 121
  { LH – 116
  LH – 117
  LH – 118
  RH – 127

3 { RH – 119
  { LH – 126

4 { RH – 121
  { LH – 115

Repeat on the right side.

Arrow indicates that point is out of the main picture – on front or side of body. Check with chart showing main Jin Shin Do points.

1 Draws tensions down through the leg, freeing the pelvis so that snarled up energy at the spinal cord has somewhere to flow, and also helping the brain to unravel its knots.
NB. point behind the knee as an indicator of the activity of the mental digestive processes of the brain.

RH = right hand. LH = left hand.

r = right side. l = left side.

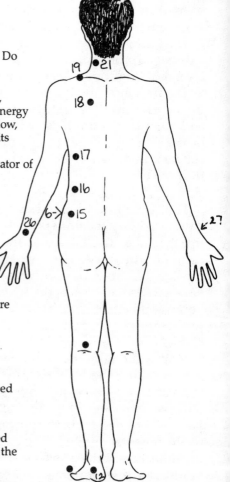

2 Frees the spinal cord via the Throat centre and also indicates condition of fear inhibiting action (16), liver or pancreas (17), emotional congestion (18), feelings about sexuality (27).

3 Further freeing of any emotions released by work on spine.

4 Makes stronger and more fluid improved interaction of energies moving between the Throat and Pelvic centres.

Figure 19

their sense of weakness and, more importantly, with the contents of their unconscious mind. To see into our unconscious can be a frightening and challenging experience; we have to be fully ready for it if we are to make good use of the experience. The Back release will soothe away emotional hurt, yet leave someone feeling calmer, stronger, clearer in understanding, and more in touch with their strength.

You may wonder why ever the Bridge would be used! But we need at times to experience the depth of our vulnerability, of our receptivity; we need to enter and explore the contents of our unconscious mind; particularly, in order to come to make friends with our spiritual identity, we need to sink down into our fear and doubt. So the Bridge is very much about our deeper integration as spiritual beings inhabiting a personality in the physical or material world. And it also has the power to drain away any excess of emotional flooding that a person may be caught in.

HIGH BLOOD PRESSURE RELEASE

Just as the Back release can be seen as a follow through or back up release to the Regulator, so the High Blood Pressure release can be seen to do this for the Bridge.

This is because both Bridge and High Blood Pressure releases are founded upon freeing the kidney-adrenal area. They both achieve a profound easing of tension and pressure in the heart area as a result of their unravelling of kidney tension.

1. The primary effect of the High Blood Pressure release is to drain and free kidney energy; this brings an easy gentling and soothing of hypertension of the heart.
2. This primary release makes possible a very profound adjustment of tensions at the head level. The flow of impulses from the right to the left hemispheres and back again is made more fluent because of the deep untangling of tension knots at the brainstem. This release is carried out through points at the neck, so the freeing of the brain takes place hand-in-hand with release of traffic jams of nerves at the Throat centre.
3. Dissipation of congestion at the brain and throat in turn make it possible for the Crown centre to achieve more vital activity. This means that a better flow of energy from the spiritual

HIGH BLOOD PRESSURE RELEASE

Standing at the head of the patient throughout ...

  First Movement:

  { LH – l22
  { RH – r16
    RH – l26
    RH – r1
    RH – top of breastbone (D)
    RH – crown (A)
    Repeat on opposite side.

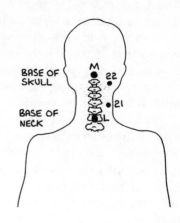

  Second Movement:

  { Both hands – 21
  { LH – l21
    RH – r3
    RH – l2
    RH – r1
    LH – l22
    RH – l1
    Repeat on opposite side.

  Third Movement:

  LH – base of neck (L)
  RH – top of breastbone (D)
  LH – base of skull (M)
  RH – above lip (C)
  RH – third eye (B)
  RH – crown (A)
  LH – heart centre
  LH – third eye (B)

RH = right hand. LH = left hand.
r = right side. l = left side.

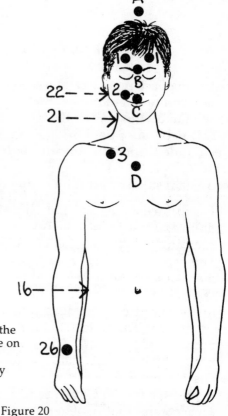

Always spend a good long time on the first link of 16 with 22 ... don't move on from the 16 until you feel energy flowing much more freely and easily through this point.

Figure 20

essence of the person is made possible. The patient finds it easier then to connect with his own spiritual identity, and to begin to find shape and expression for this through his own (now freer) Throat centre.

4. The unravelling of tensions at the throat, and the stronger stimulating inflow from the Crown centre, enables a better integration of head activity with heart activity: it becomes easier for a person's thoughts to be aligned and at-oned with their feelings.

The action of the High Blood Pressure release is very intense, using mostly short, diagonal handlinks which allow for lopsidedness in the person to be adjusted; messages can flow more readily from one side of the body to the other so that better coordination between the two sides becomes possible: a sense of centred poise and one-pointedness is more accessible to the patient.

It is a release pattern which covers only the upper body and its effect is in keeping with this as it influences the more subtle faculties. Just as brain lopsidedness is adjusted, so also emotional imbalance is affected: a patient will find himself more able to balance his feelings towards others with his feelings towards himself.

It is a pattern which is helpful when we are trying to develop a more conscious relationship with our spiritual identity. The improved alignment of thoughts and feelings makes it easier to use the mind to connect with the Soul. In this way it can help us along our spiritual journey.

The High Blood Pressure release involves three movements.

In the first movement, the base point is the 22. The other hand holds the 16 on the opposite side. This allows for a gentling and draining of adrenal activity which in turn brings a soothing of the brain. The diagonal handlink is to either side of the Heart centre and has a powerful effect in drawing pressure and tension away from here. The hand at 16 then moves across to the 26 on the same side as the base 22, further easing away tension released at the Heart centre . . . emotional tension is quickly gentled.

The next step involves the 26 changing to the 1 opposite to the base 22, which, in a short, intense, diagonal pull, frees the restless mind. Now the left hand shifts to the top of the breastbone, at the centre (releasing tension lodged between the Throat and the Heart centres and stimulating the thymus gland to better activity), whilst the right hand covers the Crown centre. Alignment of the mind with spiritual inspiration is helped.

This movement is repeated on the other side.

In the second movement the two hands begin at each 21, awakening this key Throat centre point to activity. The left 21 remains whilst the right shifts to the right 3, freeing the lower Throat centre flows; the right hand shifts to the left 2, freeing the upper Throat centre flows; the right hand moves to the right 1, freeing the consciousness, the pituitary, and the Third Eye, even more. Now the base at left 21 moves up to left 22, leaving the right hand at right 1: release of the mind and brain is carried even further, enabling better transmission from one side of the brain to the other. Finally the right 1 moves across to the left 1, completing this thorough unravelling of head tensions.

In the third movement, the right hand covers the top of the sternum and the left hand the spine where it reaches the neck (L). This further activates and clears the lower throat. The left hand moves up to the base of the skull, drawing lower Throat centre release through to the upper Throat centre. Now the right hand moves to above the upper lip (C), bringing intense release of the upper Throat centre. The right hand shifts to free the Third Eye centre (B), allowing deep relaxation of the organs at the heart of the brain, lying directly between these two points. From here it moves to the Crown, making possible a further alignment of the mental body with the Soul. The left hand now moves to the Heart centre, and then the Third Eye centre, to balance this alignment, and to reconnect the second movement, with its adjustment of the mind, with the first movement, and its release of the Heart centre.

This completes this intense adjustment of the emotional and mental faculties. You can see from the handlinks made that a strong magnetic pull will be exerted upon all glued-up areas of the brain and throat, making possible a much easier transmission of impulses. Functioning of the mind is electrical, but needs the chemical activity of the brain if it is to be carried through, or made conscious. If the brain cells are glued up through inefficient elimination of chemical wastes, the electrical activity of the mind will become limited, stilted and blurred: shorting out will occur.

Much brain difficulty is linked with adrenal inefficiency, so this pattern is able to help the brain also through its easing of adrenal tension.

It is very important to follow the High Blood Pressure release with the Neck release, even though the High Blood Pressure release uses so many neck points. This is because the intense and deep release of head and neck tensions does have the power to change a person's perceptions and vision and this may be uncomfortably disorienting until the patient grows accustomed to what seems to be a subtly changing identity. The Neck release will ease away loose threads, soothe and balance once more.

This is not a pattern that would usually be used in the early stages of treatment – although this can be appropriate. If someone has very rigid thought patterns, much resistance or scepticism, it may produce pressure or tension or even headaches . . . it may be very difficult for someone to let go of their head tension. It is safer to draw these away from the head by working on the legs. Release the legs and stimulate better digestion by paying attention to the knees. As the knees free (digestion of mental and emotional experience should also improve), it will be easier for head tensions to let go. If the Solar Plexus centre has been soothed and eased, the patient will be less subject to fear and insecurity, will be calmer in his personal emotions, making it easier for the brain to sink down into deeper and deeper surrender of tensions, or relaxation.

This release pattern combines well with the Great Central and the Belt and Penetrating, and would be used to follow either of these, being followed in turn by the Neck release, but not the Neck release with variations.

8. Shallow and Deep Uses of Release Patterns

The Regulator is appropriate to start a series of sessions, to end a series, and at any time during a series. It is a good beginner because you can trust it gently to soothe and unravel much of the surface, shallow distress that has brought your patient to you. As the sessions progress, and you reach deeper knots of tension, and begin to unravel these, it can greatly help to gentle and soothe, to 'regulate' the temporary turmoil that can often result as these deep knots are loosened and the tension that has caused the main problem is drawn up to the surface. If you feel at any stage that the energy flows of a person are getting out of control, the Regulator will quickly bring back the sense of balance and proportion. Use it frequently where you recognise poor liver functioning to be a root problem, and also when your patient's nervous system tends to become either locked with tension, or hyperactive. Finally, use it when you know you won't be working with the person again for a long time: it will leave them integrated, well-coordinated, strong to face whatever next confronts them in their life.

The Bridge is a release pattern which is used much less frequently than the Regulator, although there are some people who are 'Bridge patients' and benefit from its more frequent use. Generally, it is used at a time when the superficial picture is well under control and you feel that tangles around the Heart centre – showing through the arms, chest and lower throat area – are beginning to free, and that the person is soothed and relaxed enough for these to be more potently released. If there is rigidity in the tension of the nervous system (NB the liver state), then it is not a good pattern to use as this rigid tension will cause a holding on to the emotional residues as they surface. It is holding on to tension which causes that tension to harm and interfere with our life. If the nervous system however is quite soft and flexible, a rare depth of relaxation can be achieved through the Bridge which can get rid of lots of stale old emotional patterns and also bring the worldly personality much more in touch with the deeper spiritual identity.

It is a release which requires more skill and sensitivity in its application than the Regulator . . . the intuition must be called upon before using it, just as it will enable the patient to be more in touch with his own intuitive faculty.

Sometimes it is appropriate to use when a person is flooded with nervous emotions; when the Heart centre and the throat centre are soggy and overwhelmed with too much loose emotion; then its value works more at the surface: it will not have such a deep effect. When the emotions are tightly held onto and resisting relaxation it should not be used: help the liver to unwind first with any of the other patterns.

The Bridge has the effect of freeing the Heart centre and the Throat centre with such power because of its effect upon the kidneys and adrenals. By easing deep tension away from these organs it drains excess fear from the patient, or enables him to relax into his fear. If we can sink down into our fear, rather than contracting or tensing against it, we can reach right through it into the stillness which lies beneath it. This stillness is in a sense at the bottom of all of life and, paradoxically, we can realise in this stillness that all is one, and that all states are, in their essence, a part of the enormous being of God. This is a beautiful paradox in which the experience of isolation and of cut-off-ness that our fear creates in us can actually lead us, if we can surrender ourselves to it, into an experience of total belongingness or at-one-ment with the essence of life itself. This is why the unravelling of kidney and adrenal tension can lead us to a closer connection with our spiritual identity. If we can identify with our spiritual essence we can begin to seek our nourishment, strength and sustenance from this bottomless source and so gradually be less dependent or needy in our relationships with others, whilst also becoming more loving and more giving . . . contact with our spiritual identity always stimulates our compassion.

The Bridge, then, has a very profound and mystical role to play for those who are ready, but it is important to bear in mind that many people may take a very long time before arriving at this readiness.

The Bridge still can gently open a person to a richer flow of their own spirituality, even though they may not be conscious of this. This is because the release of the kidney area gently but deeply eases pressure to the Heart and Throat centres. A major inhibitor of a healthy inflow of spiritual force is the build-up of tensions at the Heart centre. These tensions accumulate as we experience hurt and emotional pain and let down. For some people the sense of being emotionally unwanted or rejected will begin at a very early age and will steadily become thicker and more entrenched as the life continues. These webs of personal hurt build up around the Heart centre and imprison it so that it becomes more and more difficult for the person to feel absorbed into a group, or at-oned in any social situation. But, as well as causing a growing feeling of isolation, the tight webs around the Heart centre prevent a clear or free inflow of Soulforce. This inflow from the Soul is awakened and stimulated by the higher abstract mind, the intuition, and uses the Crown centre and the right brain. To be expressed through the person and out into the world it has to reach the Heart centre. It can be radiated from here through the individual system and out to those around him.

The Bridge, by easing and soothing and draining the kidneys (the Base centre) will also allow the Heart centre to empty of hurt, and the result of this will be that Soul inflow can reach the Heart centre and stimulate this to better and richer growth and activity. This encouragement and strengthening of the Heart centre is better if the Throat centre has already been freed to some extent. Otherwise Heart centre tensions have no proper outlet and may ricochet back onto the Solar Plexus centre causing an aggravation of problems related to personal negativity and weakness.

This is one more reason why the Bridge would normally be used towards the end of any sequence of sessions.

So use the Bridge to ease and clear too much surface emotional turbulence, and use it also at a later stage when you have brought about a general and deep unwinding of the nervous system, and poise of the emotional patterns of the patient, to help him or her to let go of fear and to sink down into the emptiness in which their spiritual essence may be found. To sink down through tensions in the body allows the mind to float up into the light airy frequencies of 'Heaven', the blue pink and gold spiritual ('spiralling') essence of life.

Because the Regulator and the Bridge are quite long patterns, and cover all body areas, they would not usually be combined with another release in the same session. They must always be followed, however, with the Neck release.

The Great Central, on the other hand, is rarely used alone. Although it has a profound effect, it is short, leaving plenty of time to combine it with other patterns. If you have not a lot of time, or if your patient needs soothing and strengthening rather than an unravelling of deeper knots, it is very well combined simply with the extended Neck release. If you use these two patterns, and work slowly and patiently with each handlink, your patient should reach a profoundly calm and centred state, leaving him or her better able to understand and to act, than previously.

The Great Central can also be combined with the Belt and Penetrating and the Neck release, and with the Clear Thinking and the Neck release. It is best used to precede either of these releases and if your patient comes to you in a state of emotional shakiness or fragility, it will always adjust and balance this, thereby preparing him for a deeper, more thorough result from the following pattern, whether the Clear or the Belt and Penetrating. The Great Central is a very beautiful release to my mind because of its simplicity, and yet its ever ready appropriateness. We could happily re-name it the Great Gentle release!

You can be sure that it will re-centre the patient quickly, no matter how much deep-seated tension has surfaced from previous work . . . it is a good follow-up to the Bridge because it will be sure to ease any difficult results from this. In fact it is good to use after any session which you felt had an element of challenge about it. When you feel your own heart swelling in compassion for your patient's trials, and long to soothe these away gently, use this pattern. But also, when you feel that your patient is bravely exploring the unravelling of his or her own turmoil, and achieving this in good balance, and you don't want to over-interfere . . . when you want to stand by him in supportiveness, without imposing your self and your way . . . then use this pattern.

The Belt and Penetrating is a short but profound release which can also be used at any time with good results. It won't usually release any difficult-to-handle turmoil from the deeper regions, yet it should make possible an easier moving forth into action. Tension frequently leaves a person 'rooted to the spot' – able perhaps to see their problem, but unable to act and therefore move on through it; such inactivity causes frustration, and a draining and debilitation of energy and lifeforce. If you can help a person to act, you can help him or her to free himself from that frustration and to experience a resultant strengthening and better flow of life force.

It is not a pattern that would be used as frequently as the Great Central and does not have such a wide application. Its use is more specific, and directly to do with freeing the Pelvic centre, and the Throat centre, and the head as a further result of the Pelvic release. It can be used fairly early in a sequence of sessions, when you want to strongly stimulate the Throat centre to better activity, and to have the effect of dissipating a deep fogginess at the brain. Or if the problem your patient is specifically complaining of involves lower back problems or any difficulty in the Pelvic region . . . it can then be used to begin a series of sessions.

However, if you suspect some very deep deficiency or congestion at the Pelvic or Base centres, for instance perhaps ovarian blocks or unbalance, it is probably best to begin with the Regulator as the Belt and Penetrating could so stimulate the area that a strong cleansing may take place, for example, extra heavy bleeding, which may actually be positive, but may also frighten your patient. The Belt and Penetrating can definitely produce this kind of a physical result and the physical cleansing may also bring with it psycho-emotional symptoms related to hormones – for example depression, isolation. Where any hormonal imbalance is suspected, work gently to right this . . . try to stimulate better liver activity (Regulator, Back, Clear) and, through this, a clearer mind, before focussing directly upon ovarian functioning. This is because the hormones strongly influence our powers of perception and our emotional responses, and this can result in us experiencing our lives with too much pain. As toxins are eliminated from our bodies as a result of the cleansing stimulus of the healing work we are usually temporarily flooded with these, and with the psycho-emotional toxins they correspond with. Any toxic build-up is stored at a deep cellular level where we are not directly aware of it . . . the toxins are constantly pushed to the back of the cupboard as more come in . . . when the clearing-out comes these toxins are first emptied into the bloodstream from which the liver and kidneys must eliminate them. This process takes a little time and if the patient does not help the body (through a cleansing diet and plenty of exercise and clean air) to eliminate the load the bloodstream is now carrying, he will feel the ill-effects of the toxins . . . he will feel 'poisoned' . . . for a while. This sense of feeling poisoned will continue until the body is able to clean all the toxins out of the system.

The problem of hormonal imbalance is an organic problem – to do with the organs that govern body function. If your patient's problem is a structural one, for instance if you suspect that a nerve could be trapped at the lower spine, then you can safely and effectively begin to work immediately with the Belt and Penetrating. Follow next with the Back perhaps, to carry the Belt and Penetrating release further along the spine, and then go on to use the Regulator at the third session if the previous two have brought good results, in order to balance and realign the whole system after the interference of its patterns that your previous two sessions will have brought . . . a positive interference, but nevertheless even positive change can to some extent be disorienting.

In this example, you would benefit by combining the Belt and Penetrating with the Great Central (the Great Central comes first). If however you seek a subtle draining and easing of head fogginess, the Belt and Penetrating would be combined with the Clear, the Belt and Penetrating coming first. Sometimes you want to work more directly – yet still gently – upon the head, in which case you would combine the Great Central with the Clear. This combination is direct in its effect upon the head, and yet it is very light in its touch. The effect of the Belt and Penetrating upon the head would tend to be more profound and therefore potentially more intense. Even used early in a sequence of sessions the Belt and Penetrating and the Clear would tend to work at a deeper and more profound level than the Great Central and the Clear.

In general, if the Belt and Penetrating is being used to influence an organ problem (for example, ovarian deficiency) it will act at a deep level whereas if it is being used to adjust a structural problem, (for example, a trapped nerve), it will act at a more shallow level.

The Clear Thinking is always a light release. In itself it does not plumb the depths of congestion. And yet, in its very lightness it has the power to bring about a very profound – if 'light' – mental relaxation and ease. This release makes me think of brightness, hopefulness, playfulness and joy. Sometimes the work of unravelling one's physical, emotional and mental health knots can feel tough going . . . this release can bring a deep sense of psycho-emotional acceptance, relaxation and ease into the effort of this journey. It has a buoyant and soothing effect upon the psyche.

Used with the Belt and Penetrating (the Clear always follows), it can soothe the effects of this, and yet deepen its profundity because when soothed we relax and when relaxed we effortlessly sink deeper. Used with the Great Central and the Neck release (the extended Neck release) – the Clear comes in the middle – it brings great mental relief to someone whose psychological journey has been belaboured or shadowy.

The Back release will often work at a deep level and can stimulate a loosening of old knots which may result in some turmoil at the surface for a while. If used early in a series of sessions (for example, it is good to follow the Regulator) it will simply help to ease tensions and confusion out of the spine, enabling a better circulation through the whole nervous system and a better blood supply to all organs and muscles. It can, through draining away fuzzy congestion in the spine, help to clear the neck and brainstem and brain itself to a stronger and clearer activity. It is its direct effect upon the spine which brings an improved easing of tensions in the nervous system and this is also the key to its more profound effect. Most of us rarely achieve more than a very superficial relaxation, even in sleep, and therefore the renewal and healing of the functioning of our organs can never be more than superficial: renewal and healing can only come about when no demands are being made upon the varied cells of our body. So often our relaxation only enables very surface and peripheral tensions to be unwound. This barely keeps up with the input of tension from our highly demanding day. The Back release is able, by working upon spinal congestion, to carry us into a much deeper state of relaxation than would normally be possible for us and thereby enables a more thorough refreshment and healing and vitalisation of tissues.

The more you have prepared the ground, by easing away peripheral tensions through the Regulator and maybe other patterns, the deeper this relaxation and consequent renewal will be.

The effect of the High Blood Pressure release will be shallow when it is used for high blood pressure and the kind of haywire cross-threading of electrical impulses that takes place in the brain when someone is suffering from this. This is a very destructive state to be in as brain tissues are very delicate and refined and can very easily be damaged by impulses that are trying to move through them with a speed and impetus out of proportion to their chemistry. The High Blood Pressure release will ease out this cross-threading and enable the impulses to once more travel at a more acceptable rate, but it will not, in this case, stimulate any profound adjustment of deeper tension knots or imbalances.

It is a good release to use when there is apparent confusion and overactivity of thoughts, coupled with a disturbed heart rhythm. The Great Central and the Clear can also be used in this situation and would be more frequently appropriate. Just as you would more often use the Regulator than the Bridge, so you would more often use the Great Central and the Clear than the High Blood Pressure release. Nevertheless, sometimes you feel that your patient requires a touch that is more intense than the Regulator or the Clear, and then you use the Bridge or the High Blood Pressure release.

It is only called for when the problem is focussed at the head level as it does not have any direct effect upon body areas below the waist.

Its deep use makes possible a better flow of impulses between the two brain hemispheres, by drawing tensions out of the corpus callosum. This enables memory banks in the right hemisphere to release their content into the left hemisphere where it can be processed (the painful part let go of and the useful learning substance integrated into the fresh understanding of self and life). This process brings a better co-ordination of the two hemispheres: the two hemispheres are like eyes which are usually out of focus. The High Blood Pressure release makes it possible for them to be brought into focus. When the two hemispheres are able to focus, the Third Eye begins to be consciously active and usable.

Using the High Blood Pressure release to stimulate better deep functioning of the brain is only possible once a lot of more superficial clutter and congestion has been removed and is only appropriate in the later stages of a series of sessions. I feel that this release can also help to adjust problems such as dyslexia which result from the brain developing its wiring patterns in unusual ways, often because inflammation caused by fever leaves areas in the brain congested and unable to unfold to a normal pattern. I feel too that it can help to bring about some degree of brain repair where there has been damage. The extent of repair possible depends upon many factors:

a. The stimulation of the digestive system to optimum functioning so that the brain can receive the best quality and supply of nutrients it needs to repair damaged tissues, but also so that there can be the best possible elimination of waste products from the brain. Waste products cause blockages in the flow of energy and so they slow up and inhibit development; the brain is intricate yet small, with only a narrow passage through the neck for the supply of blood carrying away toxic wastes, and bringing cell-building nourishment; toxic wastes can quickly build up in the brain and are slow and difficult to remove, yet they dramatically impair the brain's functioning.

b. The extent to which damage has left scar tissue which may prevent and get in the way of any new growth. This scar tissue and the results of any old inflammation – for example, thick and sticky mucous – will have to be gradually cleared away before new and healthy growth can take place.

c. The diet will have to be perfectly balanced according to the individual's personal requirements – food should be able to be quickly absorbed and converted into all the forms required by that particular individual; waste by-products should be minimal and not enough to slow down the metabolic processes. Diet includes oxygen. The brain needs a plentiful supply of clean oxygen to function adequately so if a person can exercise this will greatly speed up the recovery of any partial brain deficiences.

If all these factors are present, brain re-growth can take place, yet it may be slow.

Generally speaking, a shallow effect is achieved by release patterns when they are used early in a sequence of sessions, or when they are used to adjust a tangible and fairly obvious physical and structural problem. Then the releases will act primarily upon the surface tensions and imbalances. As surface problems are eased away it will become possible to penetrate with your work to deeper and more subtle problems that will perhaps only be visible now that the more superficial condition is adjusted. As you tackle the deeper problems, so you will be able to apply the release patterns from the attitude of understanding their more profound relevance.

9. Liver and Kidney Functioning through Physical, Emotional, Mental and Spiritual Levels

INTRODUCTION

The digestive organs include the stomach, pancreas, spleen, intestines, and gall-bladder, as well as the kidneys and the liver. Each of these organs has a part to play in the conversion of food into usable fuel and repair material in the body, and also in the removal from the body of the waste remaining after conversion.

However, in this system of interpreting the balance of health, the liver and kidneys have a special role to play in the maintenance of our physical bodies as vital organs, or instruments through which our personalities can experience and unfold. This is because the physical tasks of these organs symbolise the two universal forces to which we are all responsive, as creatures of nature.

The one force is active, the other is receptive. Thus the liver is the organ which enables us to act out individuality in the world; it gives us the fiery, active energy to strive forward along our chosen path. The kidneys, on the other hand, receive impressions from our experience in our life; their task is to filter out and eliminate from the watery or emotional bloodstream of life the results of experience which represses or holds us back, just as, physically, they receive the bloodstream, then filter it of impurities and seek to expel these from the body.

If we, as healers, can assess the state of functioning of our patient's liver and kidneys, we are able to immediately understand certain things about their problems with their emotional, mental and spiritual natures. Similarly, if we can bring about a more dynamic functioning of these organs at a physical level, we can expect our patient to be much better equipped to recognise and deal with his emotional, mental and spiritual difficulties.

121

Figure 21

In emphasising these two physical organs we are not suggest-
ing that problems in the body cause problems of an emotional or
mental nature (although this can happen), but rather that by
improving the vitality of the body, the patient is stronger, more
positive and more inspired to deal with his problems at a subtler
level.

ABSORPTION AND ELIMINATION

Improved kidney and liver functioning means that the whole
body of the patient will be able to respond once more to the
natural ebb and flow of life force: he will feel more spring in his
walk, more alertness and humour in his mind, more sensitivity to
colours and sounds and indeed all body sensations. He will be
able to respond with more interest and exhilaration to what is
going on around him, be better able to deal with crises, and be
less undermined and brought down by the stresses and uncer-
tainties of life.

The reason for this is that these two organs govern absorption
and elimination. The whole digestive tract and organs deal with
the absorption of nourishment and the elimination of waste.
What gives the liver and kidneys their importance is that their
condition of contraction (tension) or relaxation (fluidity) will
determine the basic efficiency of the whole digestive system. The
rhythm of energy flowing through these two base or root organs
will condition the rhythm or pattern of flow through the whole
system. When we grow tired and weary, and have no energy to
face the day, even after a night of sleep, it is usually because we
are no longer taking into the cells of our bodies the substances
needed by them to work with vitality; and because we are no
longer able to rid our bodies of their waste products, some of
them toxic. So the various different types of cells throughout the
body become starved of nourishment, and also stiff and thick and
stuffed with rubbish. No wonder they and we, too, lack zest and
dynamism.

Both liver and kidneys are involved in absorption of nutrients
and elimination of toxins, but the liver, as the largest chemical
factory in the body, mostly influences absorption, whilst the
kidneys, as the filtering system for the bloodstream, has the
strongest effect upon elimination of waste.

It is important to hold in the mind these respective roles of the two organs, as they are the key to understanding the impact upon these organs of emotional, mental and spiritual events; but it is these two roles which are also the key to understanding how changes at the spiritual, mental and emotional levels can be carried through at the physical level.

The activities of absorption and of elimination correspond with many activities throughout the arena of life. They are like the two muscles which oppose each other on all limbs: the one pulls back or down, the other pulls forward or up. Absorption and elimination are the ways in which the active and receptive forces governing all life carry through.

So also are the inbreath and the outbreath of each of our bodies. All of life springs from and responds to this rhythm at the essence of being. It can be seen in the pattern of light and dark, sun and moon, and of summer and winter; in the rhythm of expansion and contraction, of stretching up and out as far as we can, and then shrinking, curling and tightening down and into ourselves; of space, boundless, still and immeasurable, and time, which we measure with great care and are imprisoned by; of day and night, which still demands some response from our bodies no matter how we resist this with electric lighting and central heating; of man and woman, activity and rest, life and death.

These are the forces which, when we are out of balance, we experience as duality . . . we cannot absorb the rich and nourishing experience they offer us, and yet neither can we eliminate the painful content of that experience, the toxic wasteproduct; and so we continue to be constrained and inhibited (contracted) by that pain.

When we are in balance, harmonious and at one with the world, these contrasting forces flow through us unrestrained and we are abler to sense that flow as a to and fro, wave-like motion of contraction or tension, or expansion and relaxation. We can identify the wave, and the cycle that it forms and so we can trace coherent patterns in the shape of our lives, and read meaning and understanding from these patterns which help us to more deeply and richly experience whatever comes next.

LIVER AND KIDNEYS IN TERMS OF THE PHYSICAL BODY

When thinking about the physical roles of these two organs we must remember the gallbladder and the adrenal glands.

One of the tasks of the liver is to manufacture the bile salts which emulsify fats and enable them to be absorbed into the bodily tissues. The gall-bladder stores these bile salts so that there is always an available supply when food is eaten. The gall-bladder is situated just below the inner part of the liver.

The adrenal glands sit like little hats, one on top of each kidney. They are involved in producing adrenalin and other hormones and they take some responsibility for balancing the sex hormones.

Like liver and gall-bladder, the kidneys and the adrenals have a very sensitive relationship with each other. Tension lodged in one will directly restrict the functioning of the other. This is especially important when considering the parts played by the kidneys and the adrenal glands through the physical, emotional, mental and spiritual levels of functioning. For instance, the adrenal glands and their production of adrenalin are affected by the condition of the Base centre. This will always influence kidney functioning, but also should be thought about in terms of the need in the body for a supply of adrenalin.

Tension locked at the Base centre (a very common state of affairs) will result in over-taut kidneys, which will not be able to filter the bloodstream with an easy, pulselike rhythm; it will also result in the adrenals being too tight, so that adrenalin is produced and supplied with too great effort: the flow will not be in easy response to circumstances; there may be too much sometimes, too little at others; or it may be continuous, but too thin, if the adrenals have lost the power to relax . . . they will become steadily weakened and less able to respond to shock or crisis whilst the person they belong to becomes more and more chronically tired, yet unable to unwind and relax.

THE LIVER

There are three main branches to the physical work of the liver:

a. It receives the contents of the bloodstream and rearranges the chemical contents brought to it, so that they can be used for specific purposes throughout the body. This constant synthesis of chemical forms generates heat, which, with the burning of sugar and fat, provides the body with heat and energy for activity. The liver is like a furnace, converting chemical substances into forms which the body can absorb and make use of. This task is about nourishment.

b. It produces substances which break down toxic elements so they can be removed from the body. This task is about cleansing.

c. It produces substances needed by the immune system to fight disease. This task is about protection and defence.

It is a large organ and can still perform its work even when much of it is destroyed. However, its efficiency will directly influence our capacity to respond with resilience and vitality to the experience our life confronts us with.

The liver is directly affected by our emotional experience, but certain physical factors strongly afflict it: foods combining proteins and fats (nuts, seeds, cheese, eggs), all forms of sugar, even honey; all medication and chemicals (anaesthetics, etc); vinegar; overeating; alcohol; fatty and processed foods; too much 'watery' and cold food (i.e. fruits and salads); stimulants.

Exposing the liver to any of these will often cause it to become either too tight, or too dulled. If tightness results, the liver will function quickly but with shallowness, and so its chemical processing will be incomplete. Both physical, emotional and mental activity will suffer.

The physical body will move with quick, tight movements. Muscles will be too contracted and unable to relax. Tiredness and stiffness will build up in them. We will feel impatient yet have difficulty carrying through that which we have begun. There will be a tightness also at the brain, possibly causing headaches.

The functioning of the brain and nervous system is partly electrical and partly chemical. The chemical functioning is governed by the liver's capacity to keep the chemicals needed by the brain flowing into the bloodstream in the appropriate proportions. If the liver fails to do this, because it has been submitted to something (e.g. medication, too much tahini – sesame paste rich in oil and protein) which afflicts it, the brain will not be able to carry out the chemical connections required of it by the electrical impulses seeking to pass through it. Chronic tension can build up in the brain as a result of this. This tension will transmit itself through the nervous system to the whole body.

When such tension is acute there will be a fieriness in the

rhythm of the energy flowing through the liver and a tendency for the person to respond to situations which seem to contain conflict, like an erupting volcano. This can be very exhausting and nerveracking for other people in the vicinity of this person's volcanic mood, yet it is probably healthier for that person to release their fiery tension in one outburst, however fierce it may seem.

Such tension, when held in, results in the fiery quality being transferred elsewhere in the body where it will cause a disruption of harmonious activity. Ideally such fiery energy should be directed into some creative ongoing aspect of the person's life: the fundamental role of the liver is to enable us to unfold and develop our individual, personal journey through life. If we frequently suffer from explosive liver tension it is a good idea to have a variety of ongoing projects of different kinds so that there is something we are able to direct our energy into which leaves us feeling productive and fulfilled rather than guilty.

Both indoor and outdoor sports are excellent for this, but also any activity that requires our full participation and has some obvious constructive goal. Physical activities are often more quickly effective for freeing fiery tension than mental ones.

If this fiery tension in the liver continues, perhaps because the person is not aware of what is causing it, it will eventually become its opposite. The fieriness will become a dulledness. The liver will be numb and lazy and we will experience lethargy, fatigue and depression. This is a much more serious situation, as it is more difficult to balance. Rest can ease the problem, but often a restlessness will accompany the depression which will prevent a person from being able to relax and rest. Also we always hate to feel down and will be tempted to use stimulants, to irritate some spark of life from our livers once more. This will only compound the problem as it will further disturb and distort the natural and balanced chemical activity of the liver. But also it will strengthen the tendency of the liver to swing from a too fiery and volcanic activity, to a dulled and weary and unresponsive activity.

When seeking to heal a liver condition that is causing lethargy and depression it is necessary to stimulate the liver so it can throw off the congestion it has accumulated, but also to drain away the tension that will loosen and surface as a result of this stimulation. Liver activity will probably swing from too acute tension, and the speediness that goes with this, to too dulled and quiescent activity, and the depression that accompanies this. Each swing should become less and less extreme, until the rhythm of energy flowing through the liver finds its equilibrium.

The Regulator and the Back releases are the main Jin Shin Do patterns used to adjust the rhythm of liver activity.

A plentiful supply of oxygen is extremely important for the liver and will help it to perform all its tasks smoothly and efficiently. Therefore activities which are undertaken for the sake of the liver should involve physical exercise, which causes deeper breathing out in the fresh air. Good oxygenation will both soothe and refresh the liver, enabling it to detoxify itself more quickly and completely. This detoxification will enhance all its other chemical functioning: if it is clogged and sticky with toxic substances (and 'free radicals'), it has to compete for space and raw materials with these, which get in the way of the beneficial substances it needs to produce.

Absorption is the keynote for the liver. If it is not working properly we fail to absorb all the goodness provided in our food. This in turn means that we become undernourished, even though in theory our diets may be excellent. The liver will be damaged by bad emotional experience just as much as by too great an exposure to toxic substances. Negative emotional events will start ripples of tension flowing through the liver which may make it more sensitive and intolerant to substances it is exposed to at that time. This situation can snowball so that when the liver is re-exposed to that same substance, it once more feels the painful emotions that came with it the previous time. This is a vicious cycle which can be very difficult to break.

A disturbed liver almost always results in addictive habits. There is a chemical reason for this which begins with an intolerance or allergy. If the liver is exposed to a substance which it rejects, perhaps for reasons of heredity, its chemical activity aims to break down, neutralise and eliminate that substance from the body. Liver chemistry is stimulated by the alien substance into more fierce activity than usual and the chemical agents produced by this stimulation often produce a sensation of enhanced energy in the individual. This 'high' counteracts the initial 'low' caused by the intake of the alien substance, but is followed by another 'low' as the liver rests after its extra effort of elimination.

The 'low' is unpleasant and the person often unconsciously reaches for the very substance which produced the problem in the first place, in order to recreate the high which came in the middle. The liver is steadily undermined by this pattern which very quickly has a chemical addictive control over a person. We can have an addictive dependence upon all forms of medication, drugs, alcohol, sugar, salt, stimulants such as tea and coffee, and even proteins and fats.

Rehabilitating the liver so it is freed of its addictive pattern is a very difficult process because the general energy will swing from high to low continuously and once the pattern of addiction is broken, the liver balance will be extremely sensitive and only too easily unstabilised.

Modern life is so strewn with substances which unstabilise the liver that it can be a very uneasy experience for anyone with this kind of liver sensitivity. Such people will almost always be extremely sensitive to the vibration of the spiritual plane and this will intensify their problem in the world of society.

Someone with an addictive liver will probably suffer poor absorption of nutrients. The liver is so busy trying to neutralise the antagonistic substance, and to clean the remains from the body that it is unable adequately to set the scene for good absorption of nutrients.

It is always functioning on red alert, and having to detoxify and eliminate at a tremendous rate. Inadequate chemical activity and food metabolism at the liver will mean that extra work is given to other parts of the body. There will be general strain upon the whole system which will also suffer from forms of malnutrition as a result of poor absorption of some nutrients.

The immune system will be under strain as it is constantly stimulated by being exposed to the allergen. This will leave it with less resilience to cope with infections as they come along. The lymphatic system will usually become chronically clogged, making for slow recovery from infections.

All systems in the body, the lymphatic, the immune, the digestive and the nervous systems (and, of course, the reproductive) have their own specialised tasks to perform, but also help or hinder each other to work smoothly and without hitches as a complex but subtle network of interconnecting rhythms and harmonies. A problem, or lack of rhythm in one will quickly affect the working of the others, and, therefore, of the whole.

KIDNEYS AND ADRENALS

There are two main functions of this pair of organs which we will emphasise here, as they are specifically relevant to the principle that we are considering.

a. The kidneys filter the bloodstream of impurities.
b. The adrenals produce adrenalin, some in response to a hormone secreted by the pituitary, but some in direct response to immediate events as these challenge the muscles to activity. Adrenalin is the chemical spark which enables numerous other connections to be made throughout the body. Without this spark many activities essential to life could not be carried out.

The kidneys and adrenals are about receptivity to the flow of life. Even though the adrenals produce adrenalin, the agent which stimulates the most rapid response of alert activity from the body, it does so as a result of receiving messages from the environment; so at root even the adrenals are a response mechanism. The kidneys receive the bloodstream as it is distributed through the body. They filter all the unwanted surplus garbage from the bloodstream, allowing it to continue its flow, fresh and clear of impurities, and redirecting the waste to be expelled from the body.

Tension will immediately build up in the kidneys as a response to threatening or upsetting emotional experience. This tension will prevent the filtering system from continuing in a rhythmic, harmonious way. Some impurities will escape the filter and return into the body. The kidneys will not be able to maintain cleanliness in themselves and will become furred up or clogged, further restricting their efficient functioning.

If the bloodstream is very laden with waste products tipped into it by the liver in its work of metabolising food and detoxifying the blood, the kidneys may be unable to cope with filtering out such a load. The excess will go to the lymphatic system and the skin. If these, too cannot cope with the extra load, impurities will in time have to be stored away deep in cell tissue.

This is what happens when the body is constantly exposed to more waste products than the liver and kidneys can deal with. They are pushed to the 'back of the cupboard', to be tidied away some other, less busy day. But if alien matter continues to come into the body, both liver and kidneys are kept busy and that day never comes. The body becomes steadily more clogged with unwanted matter, and steadily less efficient also. Cleaning such an overloaded system takes time and dedication and is usually quite an uncomfortable process as all the old waste has to be released into the bloodstream, where it will be more close to the surface of the body until it can be eliminated. The kidneys will by now lack tone and so it may take some time for them to properly remove the excess. The person will experience the toxic effects of the impurities he is trying to eliminate until they can be fully shed away.

Tension in the adrenals will result in an uneven flow of adrenalin. Sometimes there will be too much and at other times not enough. This will reduce the smooth flexibility with which a person is able to respond to situations, in particular crises and stress. A person may find himself over-reacting to quite minor stresses, yet unable to react to other, more far-reaching ones.

At first tension at the adrenals will result in a tendency for them to be shaky and a bit too sensitive to crisis, or potential crisis. If the tension continues, because perhaps this person does not know how to unwind, or cannot get rest from the stress, the adrenals will become tight, but dulled: this person will shrink into himself and away from situations of potential challenge, whilst at the same time becoming less and less able to deal creatively or expansively with life events. The urge for security and safety will strengthen and the life-direction will be more and more governed by fear.

Releasing the tension that has produced dulled adrenals is a very delicate process, requiring a sensitive touch from the whole being of the healer. Bringing the adrenals to a state of better stability involves exposing the patient to his own fear, insecurity and sense of vulnerability.

Often tension in the adrenals and kidneys begins as a response to extreme shock or trauma, often in the very early years of life, when the brain is not developed enough to rationalise or make coherent the traumatic events. Freeing the adrenals-kidneys from such deep shock has to result in the patient re-visiting in some way or another, the incident which caused the shock. Successfully integrating this into the current life-attitudes will however result in greatly improved strength and stability of kidney-adrenal functioning. Many secondary health problems will melt away as a result.

Many health problems such as arthritis, psoriasis and some

cancers originate from a breakdown in kidney-adrenal function-ing as a result of deep shock.

Kidney-adrenal tension always has an adverse effect upon the heart. There will be a characteristic flutteriness to the energy flowing through here; it will often be very fast and too light and thin. Improving heart functioning is often best brought about by gently soothing and easing away tension lodged at the kidneys.

If the adrenals are not able to maintain a relaxed production of adrenalin, because they are caught in too tight a tension-state, the other organs throughout the body will be inefficiently supplied with this essential hormone and so they in turn will function under imperfect conditions and their work will suffer as a result. The heart however is the organ most directly affected by kidney tautness, just as the brain is the organ most directly affected by liver tension.

On the whole, the kidneys are more sensitive to our emotional experience, whilst the liver is more sensitive to our thought and physical life. The kidneys will contain within their cells the pattern of tension brought from any previous life and this fact further deepens the need for a sensitive touch when seeking to relax kidney tension.

The Bridge, and High Blood Pressure releases are the release patterns which most directly influence the kidneys.

THE PHYSICAL RELATIONSHIP BETWEEN THE LIVER AND KIDNEYS

As we travel along the path of our life, events take place around us. We respond to these events with a release of adrenalin from the kidney-adrenals; this adrenalin stimulates the liver to convert glycogen into immediately available energy which is then carried in the bloodstream to all parts of the body which need fuel to burn so that action can be made. The actions we make then are our statement of individuality in the world. These actions pro-duce a response from the world which we in turn must respond to. This is the sequence of events, expressed in the crudest of terms, which takes place continuously.

The two organs, the kidneys and the liver, will strive to work as one cooperating team, but where there is any tension build-up within them, this will be difficult to achieve. If there is enough

LIVER & KIDNEYS THROUGH PHYSICAL, EMOTIONAL & SPIRITUAL LEVELS CHART I

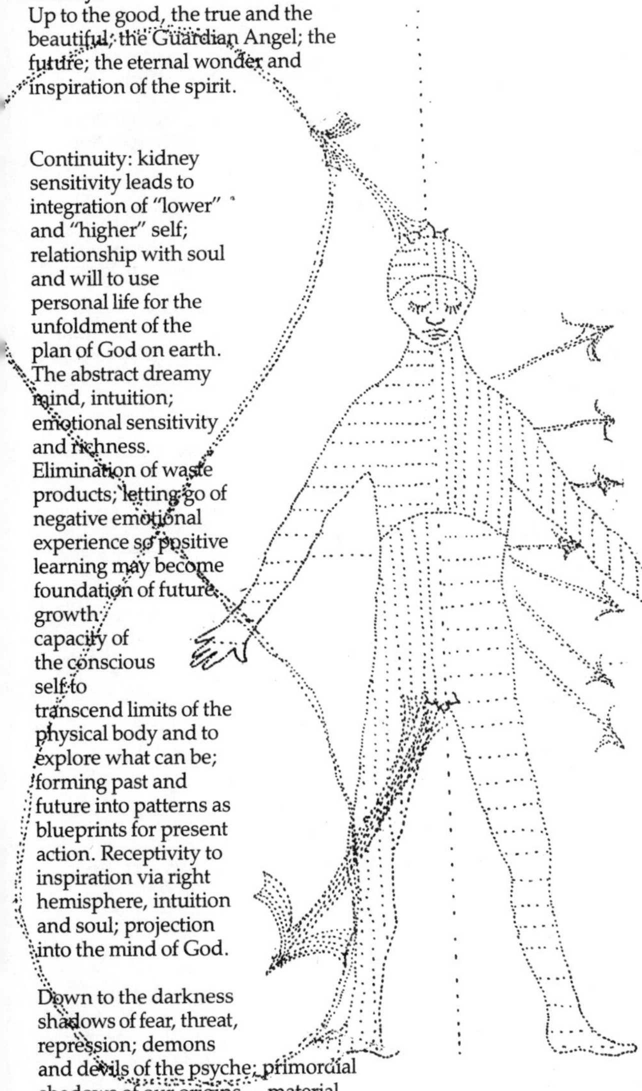

Kidneys
Up to the good, the true and the beautiful; the Guardian Angel; the future; the eternal wonder and inspiration of the spirit.

Continuity: kidney sensitivity leads to integration of "lower" and "higher" self; relationship with soul and will to use personal life for the unfoldment of the plan of God on earth. The abstract dreamy mind, intuition; emotional sensitivity and richness. Elimination of waste products; letting go of negative emotional experience so positive learning may become foundation of future growth; capacity of the conscious self to transcend limits of the physical body and to explore what can be; forming past and future into patterns as blueprints for present action. Receptivity to inspiration via right hemisphere, intuition and soul; projection into the mind of God.

Down to the darkness shadows of fear, threat, repression; demons and devils of the psyche; primordial shadows of our origins – material for present and future growth and unfoldment.

Liver
Personal ego; outward and wordly self; drive to personal expression and fulfilment.

The physical brain, the mind, the intellect; physical vitality.

Absorption of nourishment and of learning elements from experience towards future unfoldment.

The present focus of self in the NOW; action and order in terms of tangible present conditions. Carrying into action of inspiration coming from right hemisphere and kidney receptivity.

Chart V

LIVER & KIDNEYS THROUGH PHYSICAL, EMOTIONAL & SPIRITUAL LEVELS CHART II

Spiritual Fire

A Ability to tune in to inflow of spiritual (high) frequency from Soul : receptivity to this.

B Suicidal tendencies; reluctance to respond to Soul's will to exist in a body, and to carry through its plan for that personality upon earth.

A Form is given to Spirit. Expression of spiritual identity. Acting out of spiritual will. Transmission of high frequency energy.

B Action towards self-protection resulting in separativeness from others and rawness of life; separation from spirit; inability to safely transmit high frequency energy.

Mental Air

A Right hemisphere and intuition. Ability to quickly clear unneeded contents of past experience and to project positive will onto future.

B Isolation from deeper self and others; fear of rejection; refusal to accept responsibility for own pain or hardship.

A Left hemisphere and intellect. Ability to deal quickly and efficiently with ongoing circumstances; to quickly integrate lessons of past in a positive way with present events.

B Nervous attitude; inability to readily identify with others; sense of rejection yet actions which bring rejection. Frustration and anti-social behaviour.

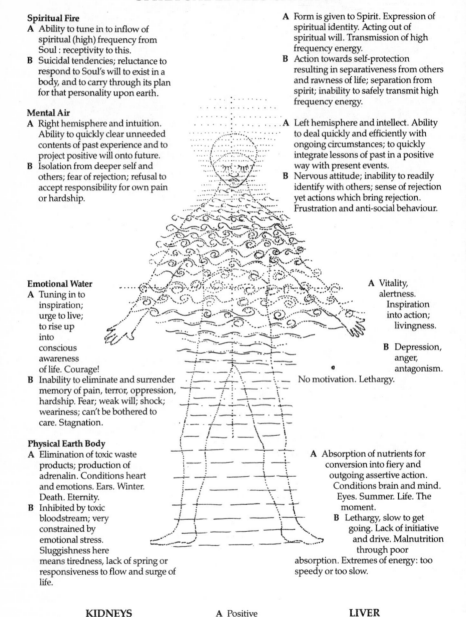

Emotional Water

A Tuning in to inspiration; urge to live; to rise up into conscious awareness of life. Courage!

B Inability to eliminate and surrender memory of pain, terror, oppression, hardship. Fear; weak will; shock; weariness; can't be bothered to care. Stagnation.

A Vitality, alertness. Inspiration into action; livingness.

B Depression, anger, antagonism. No motivation. Lethargy.

Physical Earth Body

A Elimination of toxic waste products; production of adrenalin. Conditions heart and emotions. Ears. Winter. Death. Eternity.

B Inhibited by toxic bloodstream; very constrained by emotional stress. Sluggishness here means tiredness, lack of spring or responsiveness to flow and surge of life.

A Absorption of nutrients for conversion into fiery and outgoing assertive action. Conditions brain and mind. Eyes. Summer. Life. The moment.

B Lethargy, slow to get going. Lack of initiative and drive. Malnutrition through poor absorption. Extremes of energy: too speedy or too slow.

KIDNEYS	A Positive	LIVER
	B Negative	

Chart VI

tension in either or both organs, they may even work against each other.

Together they are the foundation upon which the stability and vitality of the individual rest. Any attempt to adjust poor activity anywhere in the whole being must take into consideration the condition of and relationship between these two organs, and will need to bring about an improvement in their working if it is to be successful.

LIVER AND KIDNEY ACTIVITY FROM THE ANGLE OF THE EMOTIONS

Water in the planet is the element which enables communication to take place. It allows information of both a substantial and a subtle nature to flow to and from all parts of the planetary system. It is therefore the element which enables relationship to exist between the parts of the planetary organism.

Fluid in the body has exactly the same function and in the complex organism of the personality, the emotions perform this task. The emotional nature is simply water in a subtler, less obvious or tangible form. Its function is also to carry information between the different parts of the organism. The emotional nature in itself has no shape or form; yet it has the most sensitive capacity to respond and be moulded by any shape or form impressed upon it. It is able then to carry this shape or form, as a vibration, across and through itself. The emotional, or watery element within the human being in this way picks up the vibratory input of the mind (the element of air) which is in the form of thought and carries this across to the body (the element of earth), where it stimulates action.

Communication cannot take place between the mind and the body without this intermediary, relating participation of the emotions. Within this context, the liver and the kidneys each have a part to play.

The liver is responsible for carrying inspiration into action; but it is the kidneys which receive, or sense the inspiration, and pass across the spark which ignites the liver into burning the fuel necessary for action. This inspiration can come from the mind of the individual, or it can be an impetus sparked off by some event in the environment. Whether coming from within or without, there is a stimulus to action.

If the stimulus is of a threatening, or oppressive nature, the kidneys will respond with fear. There will then be a delay before they are able to pass the spark across to the liver which will enable the body to act. When the kidneys respond with fear, the liver action, when it comes, will be coloured with anger. This is necessary for the survival of the individual in an animal-like, territorial situation.

Threat to the life of the individual for reasons of competition and territory would have been the dominant note in social life in far-off days; but even now it is still extremely present, sometimes in more subtle forms, sometimes not. For example, in modern urban life it is necessary to keep a close watch on one's property for fear of it being stolen; it is often also necessary to keep close watch upon one's mate for fear he or she is not also stolen away! Anger is a sudden, fiery release of energy; the liver needs to be able to produce this quick, dynamic release so that the body can leap into instant self-defensive or aggressive action.

This interaction of liver and kidneys stems from the potential threat to the individual from other life, and the will to survive. But this team of organs is equally urged to activity by a more subtle stimulus.

When we awaken in the morning to clear sunshine and fresh, crisp air and the sound of birdsong greeting the day, our kidneys respond 'sympathetically', or with the same feeling; the urge to get up and feel the life of the new day flowing through us transmits the spark of action across to the liver which sets about burning the fuel which enables our bodies to stretch and move and rejoice, through movement and action, in the new day.

This, of course, is the pattern when the waters of our emotional life are clear and bright, free of silt and ebbing and flowing with a natural, easy motion. Mostly, however, the ocean of our emotions is murky and polluted, greasy and sluggish. When the receptive kidneys fail to eliminate the mass of waste products that have accumulated in the bloodstream (or emotional life), from a liver unable to separate out nourishment from rubbish (or good, learning experience from bad or destructive experience), they can no longer generate the spark which stimulates the liver to vital activity.

In terms of the emotions, what this means is that the kidneys are unable to eliminate and expel from the ocean of the emotional life their memory of pain, threat, oppression and repression. They cannot therefore any longer respond either to the surging thrill of life each day: the basic urge to live weakens and even dies. This in turn results in the liver functioning more and more sluggishly: it is more and more difficult to feel exhilarated by life or to be moved to anger . . . the liver (the one who lives) lacks livingness.

There are many variations on this theme, the most common one being: when we come into the world the liver's first task is to provide the materials which enable our bodies to grow healthy and strong. As life goes on it becomes more and more responsible for developing in us the individual characteristics that are personal to us: our selfhood, or 'I'-ness.

This will inevitably from time to time result in us attracting antagonistic action from the people around us. In order to fit into the particular social mould we are a part of we will be at times corrected, told off and even punished. These events counteract the urge of our liver nature towards the pursuance of our individuality.

For many, the social climate in the early years will be very antagonistic and there will be a continuous repression of the exploration to individuality: the people around us will have the habit of contradicting and negating all our expression of 'I'-ness.

If the kidneys are not also afflicted with an over-burdening of fear, threat and terror, we will probably acquiesce with the demands of our environment, holding in our selfhood until we are old enough to break free. We will then make a clean break from our repressive families and step out with courage and determination to form our own life according to our idea and inspirations.

However, if our early experience includes not only oppression, but also too constant fear, threat, violence and trauma (especially sex abuse), our personal will to live will be afflicted and it will be very difficult for us to generate the motivation or urge to get up and go out into the world to form our own personal pattern of life. We will easily become prisoners to other, dominant personalities, nevertheless feeling resentful and victimised all the while.

Many people will try to shut out the results of their trauma and then great rigidity will develop in the kidneys. There will be a strong will, but it will be stiff and inflexible and the person will be inclined to snap into panic when things get out of control. Panic comes about when the kidney state is too brittle and unstable from long-repressed fear. The person cannot feel confidence in his ability to deal with sudden unexpected demands.

There will be a need to feel in control of everything in life, and possibly also to bully others.

Fear is the emotion that tends to cling to the kidneys, whilst anger clings to the liver. If these are not lived out soon after they are experienced, they will cause a stiffening and inflexibility of these two fundamental organs. If fear accumulates around the kidneys they will eventually become too numb to respond with sensitivity to the wonder of life. There will be a deep down weariness, an inturned and lethargic attitude. Unconscious fear will influence all a person's responses. Shock acts upon the kidneys in a similar way and can be the originating influence for such health problems as arthritis, cancer, psoriasis. The kidneys work in a very limited or distorted way after an experience of great shock, or of too continuous stress.

If the liver is repeatedly prevented from acting out its forward-moving drive, or its anger, it will be unable to provide a steady, even flow of energy for the workings of the body. Anger contained within the liver will at first result in a spasmodic and volcanic release of energy. If the containment of the anger continues, there will follow a depression of mood. In time, if this also continues there will be numbness and the person will feel neither particularly angry or depressed: a general lack of emotional aliveness will steadily take over.

In order to bring the liver and kidneys into a state of balanced working order, lodged fear and anger will have to be drained away. This can only be done bit by bit. Each release will bring a change in the working mood of the organ. There will tend to be a swing from one extreme to the other. A liver that has been repressed enough to become de-pressed will begin to express extreme fieriness, or anger, in spasms; after a while it will swing the other way to stillness or unresponsiveness, to the point even of depression; in time it will swing again towards fieriness. The expression of these swings will become steadily less extreme until at last the liver finds its own point of harmonious equilibrium. It will then respond with appropriateness to whatever the current stimulus in the environment, or within the personal inspiration, may be.

The kidneys, similarly, will swing from irrational, severe attacks of fear and self-doubt, to exhaustion and stillness and back again; each swing will be less severe, until they too find their best natural equilibrium.

The initial distortion in the functioning of these two organs will usually come from a lack of clarity in the emotional life. If it continues, though, it will be as much a physical problem as an emotional one. The physical weakness caused by the emotional experience will change the emotional nature in a negative way. It is more important to release the problem at the physical level than at the emotional. If the physical organs are enabled to work with greater vitality the emotions once more begin to move and flow and the physical body is more free and able to express those emotions, or 'press them out of' the body and into action.

If release is first sought in the emotions, these are stimulated, but have nowhere to go, because the body remains blocked. The stagnation in the emotional life may change into turmoil, but the distress of the patient will continue until the bodily state is adjusted and the stale old rubbish in the emotional life can be eliminated through the body.

The kidneys and the heart are both organs of the watery or emotional aspect. Therefore these will sufer from a congested emotional life more than the liver. The liver will be more affected by the mind and thoughts of the individual. If we remember that the liver governs absorption whilst the kidneys govern elimination, we can see that a stagnant and congested emotional life is more the result of poor elimination of the waste products of experience, whilst a badly functioning mental faculty prevents absorption of the meaningful lessons of experience.

The waste products of our emotional experience are all to do with the feelings that isolate us from others: hurt, rejection, fear, doubt, inconstancy. These are the feelings that we cannot help but experience, yet must learn to eliminate and flush out of our systems, as quickly as possible. If we do not, they poison us and we can only see and feel life through an exaggerated interest in our self and our needs. If we become cut off from others through emotions of fear and hurt, our Heart centres fail to unfold which in turn cuts us off from any ability to sense the constant flow of nourishment emanating from the heart of God, through the Soul and through our own Heart centres. Our sense of isolation becomes more and more extreme and our lives deteriorate into a desperate effort to sustain our crippled selfhood. This is a very tragic state and yet all too frequent.

Freeing and then strengthening the kidneys is the route whereby it can be healed, yet it is a delicate route to take, because the inflexibility and rigidity of the kidney energy will be extreme . . . in order to survive the patient will have had to develop an ironcast will of a self-centred kind; if this can be relaxed, it will be followed by a flood of fear and vulnerability and panic which may be crippling for a while. Such a person would not usually seek healing and would need much work before the kidneys would relax; during the catharsis of kidney relaxation there would need to be much emotional support and reassurance always available.

When the process of flushing the kidneys of pain and hurt is well under way, the liver will function better and the patient will find himself better able to absorb the lessons of his experience, and to integrate these into new personality growth. It is a slow and delicate process, yet in time he will recognise a fresh richness in his capacity to respond to his life, and will cease from shrinking away from potential negative experience, knowing that even though these may cause temporary difficulty and insecurity, they will in time add to his depth of understanding and ability to participate fully in all the subtle shades and hues that life has to offer.

LIVER AND KIDNEY ACTIVITY FROM THE ANGLE OF THE MIND

The mind is to the body just as the air is to the Earth, and matter; as water links air to Earth, so the emotions link the mind to the body. Air is the element in which the idea is formed. It does not produce the idea itself, but enables the idea to take on its first ephemeral shape; this blueprint is then transmitted or carried through water (or emotional, feeling response), into earth (or body), and the field of action, activity and growth. Here the original idea can take on substance; it becomes visible and tangible and an independent functioning agent of life-force.

When we look at the sky we don't usually see ideas forming; yet if we are open to watching the sky, we may find the shapes of clouds drifting across the enormous, mysterious expanse inspiring all kinds of images in our minds. These images will often be awe-inspiring, uplifting, or soothing and dreamy. Most of us will have watched, entranced, as a particularly beautiful dawn or sunset unfolds before us, leaving us somehow re-energised with a sense of the wonder and beauty of life. How different the quality of our daily lives might be if we could, each day, take time out to breathe in the inspiration of a beautiful dawn and sunset! The sense of wonder and beauty would inspire in us the will to act out each moment of our daily lives in their image of joy and love.

But instead our lives are impressed with a sense of insecurity, isolation, and a craving for compensation in material terms for what we deprive our spirits of. We fill our skies and our air with poisonous, clogging, chemical wastes which give us only grey blurs and obscurity to gaze at instead of the array of colour, vivid and subtle, which should be our birthright as creatures of Earth. Our minds respond by getting caught in grey and deadening thought-patterns and attitudes.

It is the oxygen in air which is of particular importance to all forms of life. Air penetrates water; water carries air down into the earth; life forms absorb oxygen from the air as it is carried, both on the surface of the earth and also deep down inside it. In the human body oxygen is carried by the watery bloodstream through all groups of cells, enabling them to carry out their respective tasks.

It is this mingling of oxygen with the body that makes growth and unfoldment possible. Air is carried by water into commun- ion with earth and the result is further growth and unfoldment, through activity. The activity in turn results in a further inbreath- ing of air so that the cycle continues, always spiralling upwards to a more and more subtle and profound experience and learning.

Inspiration (air) enriches our emotional (water) experience which carries the inspired idea into our bodies (earth) which in turn awaken with an urge to make visible and tangible and real the idea we are inspired with. We leap into activity in response to this urge and all our sensitivities and knowledge are gathered together and held focussed in order to successfully carry out our desire to make visible to others our inspiration. Our experience and understanding grow and are steadily deepened and enriched by this effort to carry through our inspiration. This is true even if our attempt is unsuccessful. If we can learn from our failure our next attempt will be more refined, more aware of the complex forces we seek to harness in our efforts. Our actions will be modified, but more profound, as time unrolls.

If the body does not receive enough oxygen (frequently the case in this age of polluted skies, and stale, centrally-heated buildings and sedentary life-style), it becomes sluggish and lacks the urge to leap and bound through life. All functions in the body become slow and without spark. We frequently feed ourselves stimulants (tea, coffee, alcohol, sugar products) in the hope of arousing the spark once more. But oxygen is what we lack, and stimulating substances cannot replace this. Eventually our organs become chronically weak and lacking in tone and are then unable to respond properly to oxygen even when they do receive it.

This pattern corresponds with the non-physical scenario: If our minds do not receive the inspiration they need, they turn in upon themselves, self-analysis becomes obsessive and destructive and turns often to criticism of those around one; an attitude of criticism, rather than creative humour and companionship in our shared human state, develops and we find ourselves imprisoned and controlled by negative thought patterns.

We have become used to looking to each other and the products of our civilisation for inspiration. We have almost forgotten how to recognise the creative works of God as they are found in pollution-free sky, land and sea-scapes that have not been distorted by man, and to derive inspiration for our lives from these. There is a language in the forms of Nature, a language which speaks to us, reassures, encourages and nourishes us . . . it is the language of God. But we have sought to protect ourselves so much from the rawness of Nature, to defend and shelter our weakness from her power, which can be awesome and destructive, that our eyes and ears can no longer respond to that language.

Consequently we look to the works of man for inspiration and these are mostly based on a kind of gossipy interest in what the next person is doing, whether through writing, painting, music, dance, clothes, homes or any aspect of self-expression. We reflect and react to our neighbour's lifestyle and become caught in looking for inspiration from reflected reflections of reflections.

It becomes very difficult to live our lives from any point of reality which is integrated with the whole of life and its source. We lack identity and therefore any sure basis for true creative action. The only way through this disintegration of self is to seek inspiration from the source of life (which is also its whole). To achieve this we need to clarify and revitalise our minds, as the mind, the airy element in the individual personality, is the arena in which the idea (inspired from the Divine Life) becomes a blue-print, a skeleton essence which can give shape to action.

In order to understand how the liver and kidneys affect mental activity we need to consider the structure of the mind. The mind itself is not physical. It is an organ formed, not of physical substance, but of energy wavelengths. It acts as a receiver and transmitter according to the laws of electricity. The brain in the body is the physical organ which converts the electrical impulses of the mind into chemical messengers which activate and coordinate bodily activity. Brain and mind work together as one unit whenever possible. The brain responds mostly to the 'lower, concrete mind', which deals with the outer world of tangible effects, or that which is obvious and 'real' to all; whilst the mind responds mostly to the 'higher, abstract mind', which is involved with the unseen, intangible world of the Divine Life, and that which causes or brings about and sustains life upon Earth.

The brain itself also includes two aspects: the right and left hemispheres. The left hemisphere handles information that concerns our day-to-day, practical and personal existence, whilst the right hemisphere deals with that which lies beyond our immediate and physical survival.

This means that the right hemisphere will store all our memories of past experience, both personal and also racial. Most of such memories sink below the threshold of consciousness, yet continue to influence our personalities from an unconscious level. The right hemisphere can become cluttered with a lot of memories of difficult experience which we were not able to process and integrate when it happened. Such clutter will create tension in us and cause our actions to be dominated by anxiety, fear, phobias and depression which seem irrational yet cannot be got rid of.

Eventually things will get so bad that we will be forced to take some action. This will involve a gradual process of spring-cleaning of the right hemisphere of the brain.

We can only properly do this by remembering all the events which were too painful to deal with at the time. Because it is the painful stuff that we cannot deal with, this is what tends to fill the unconscious mind. Much of this experience is not necessary to us – we don't need to keep carrying it around. Indeed we cannot keep growing as personalities unless we identify the positive elements in all our experience, programme this into our brains under 'qualities learnt from such and such an experience', and build this learning into our ever deepening and unfolding characters. It is the pain and hurt that we don't need to keep on dragging around. So we have to remember what happened (unfortunately this always means remembering the hurt also), analyse our own part and that played by others with all the honesty we can muster, recognise what we needed to learn from the experience, store this learning back in the right hemisphere, as an essential pattern, and discard all the negative attributes of the experience.

This process can take some time and can also carry us on strange journeys down the corridors of life in all its varied garments. If we pursue the adventure with energy and determination (often from desperation), we will be brought eventually out of the darkness of our personal anguish and into the light of discovery: because the right hemisphere as well as being the storehouse of all our past experience, is also the gateway to the intuition and the world of the spirit, and the Divine Life. The journey through the darkness of our past, that takes us down into the underworld of the shadows of human fear and anguish, is a spiral which leads us eventually up into the radiant wonder and beauty of the Divine Self, and the source of all life, our own included.

As we begin to move towards this bright reality which is our connection with the Divine Life, we begin to see our past experience, painful or otherwise, as layer upon layer of fertile soil, generations of leaf mould, the experience of each season of growth, rotted down and now providing the rich material from which our current creative unfoldment can spring. When we can recognise this principle, that our past experience nourishes and enriches our present, no matter how difficult it has been, we begin to cease from tearing obsessively at old wounds; we begin to see our hardships as history from which we have come to understand so much. Our unfed needs may remain to some degree (– who amongst us have needs utterly fulfilled!), yet we can nourish the present with the understanding we have gained, and derive nourishment ourselves from exploring ways to apply and express that understanding in life.

This endeavour in turn draws us closer and closer to the source of ourselves, and of life itself, and this closeness steadily inspires and enriches our efforts. So the downward and negative spiral is transformed into an upward and positive creative unfoldment.

The left hemisphere of the brain also stores information about our experience, but only for the short-term. Its task is to deal with what is happening now. Its ability to do this will be directly influenced by the condition of the right hemisphere.

If the right hemisphere is tight with knots of tension resulting from years of unhappiness that we were never able to deal with at the time, the left hemisphere will also function in a tight and knotted way. It will be always contracting against the pressure of right hemispheric contents seeking to be released into and eliminated through its space. But also patterns of fear, self-defence and anger will form in the flow of impulses in the left hemisphere and the day-to-day unfoldment of life will be seen and responded to always through these patterns which will have developed as a result of past difficulty. If these patterns are not unravelled and new, more joyful rhythms of mental functioning established, the old, shadowy and negative ones will become stiffer and stiffer, and more and more rigid as life goes on. Such a one may reach later life poisoned and embittered and unable to recognise the good things abounding around them.

Although the unravelling of painful contents in the right hemisphere can be a difficult challenge to embark upon and carry through, yet it makes it possible for our perception of the world and our life in it to change, quite dramatically sometimes. Our consciousness changes and so also does our experience. We begin to make contact with the mind of God, to receive inspiration from that level which enhances all our awareness and enables us to work creatively upon Earth.

The true relationship between the right hemisphere and the left hemisphere should be: the right hemisphere is attuned always to the 'Word of God', as focussed through the Soul. This word is emitted as a rhythm of wavelengths which the intuition (right hemisphere) receives (or hears: ear and kidneys); this is then transmitted to the left hemisphere (intellect) where the rhythm is translated into an image (the rhythm is seen: eye). The image is then converted into action in the arena of the world. Ideally the right hemisphere should be always receiving new vision and deeper understanding from the Divine realm which it feeds continuously into the left hemisphere for expression in the life. If this is indeed what is happening for us we never become stale; there will be moments of rest and stillness, but not of staleness or of boredom.

The left hemisphere will mirror what it sees outside itself, in the life of the world, but it will not be overshadowed or governed by this. It will always fit the mirrored reflection of the world situation (the microcosm from the angle of the Universe) into the context of the wider, macrocosmic life as mirrored thorugh the right hemisphere. It will bring into focus these two visions of reality and from this will emerge the appropriate path of action for the now; (this focussing of the two 'eyes' of the mind is carried out by the Third Eye).

When the two eyes of the mind are at-oned in this way we are well on our way to fulfilling our spiritual destiny, and this is at root the goal of anyone who embarks upon any form of therapy.

So how do the liver and kidneys find their place in this?

The liver is directly linked with left hemispheric and brain functioning. When we recognise that the liver in our patient is not working as it should, we also immediately know that his physical brain will reflect the very same condition: if the liver is too undermined and clogged with longterm medication, the brain will also suffer from toxic neurones and thick and dulled activity. This in turn will tell you that this patient will tend to have difficulty applying his intellect to order and adjust the events in his life and that there will doubtless be blind spots in his understanding of these.

This theme works the other way around: if the left hemisphere tightens itself against input from the right hemisphere (because this is too painful or unwanted), and if such tightening lasts for a long period of time, the liver will suffer; it will be unable to carry out its tasks with fluency because the tension of the left hemisphere will be transmitted to it through the emotional nature and nervous system. When the liver tension goes on and on and is not dealt with, it will itself cause more tension to build up in the brain: a vicious cycle will grip the patient.

When treating someone in this situation it is always necessary to adjust the liver itself first. This will immediately have a positive effect upon the brain. Once you feel the liver is doing its job properly you can begin to assess how much resistance still lies in the left hemisphere. If there is a considerable amount of negativity, rigid thinking and reluctance to take responsibility for the life, or for healing of the self, it is worth considering whether there might be difficult karmic patterns brought through from other lifetimes, needing to be dealt with in this lifetime, but actually not being tackled. This will be apparent if there is consistent strong activity in the right hemisphere, but a tight tight knot in the left hemisphere which refuses to soften and melt away: the activity in the right hemisphere is the refusal of the corresponding left side cells to surrender and let through the information contained in the specific right hemispheric area. Such a situation cannot be forced: seek steadily to relax the kidneys so that fear can be transformed into courage and work peripherally rather than directly upon the head.

The efficiency with which the liver can supply the blood with the ingredients needed by the body, will directly influence the way the brain is able to work. If the liver chemistry is unbalanced, and the bloodstream then carries substances inappropriate to cellular needs, the very very delicate nerve cells of the brain will be flooded with these inappropriate substances. Their activity will be adversely affected and damage can even result, especially where the liver and bloodstream have been exposed to drug medication. There is a blood-brain barrier which is designed to keep unwanted materials away from the brain. But many will nevertheless leak through and also the cells of this barrier will distort and be unable to carry out their task if they are exposed to too many substances that they have not been formed to deal with. If we fill our bodies up with rubbish they will work like rubbish! I don't mean to suggest that all medication is bad, or always bad. However, it is often used haphazardly and out of desperation and ignorance when it should be used only in full awareness of its effects upon the organs and the immune system. Multitudes of lives have been saved through medication, but numerous other problems have evolved because of its too indiscriminate use.

The liver has great significance in terms of the development of the ego. Being the organ which enables us to carry our inspiration out into action, it is similarly the organ which enables us to make our statement of selfhood to the world. If this is undermined through too frequent negation in our early, formative years, our brains will crystallise into patterns which reflect rigid weakness and dependence, but also the attitude of being a victim.

The eye reflects the condition of the liver, and also of the mind. If the white of the eye is clear and smooth, and the iris bright and expressive, the thought also will be clear, fluid and bright.

The kidneys connect with the right hemisphere, and therefore the intuitive faculty. For most of us, the kidneys are very inhibited in their functioning through years and years, even lifetime upon lifetime, in which fear has dominated our experience. The kidneys are the root of our being. When we are born they bear the imprint of our past life history: their functioning in this life is affected by this.

Fear has dominated the experience of being human ever since

the dawn of our life upon Earth. When one seeks to soften and relax tension in the kidneys, one is reaching into the primordial depths of human fear. This fear inhibits and blocks the natural flow of the intuition into our right hemispheres. Since it is through the right hemisphere that we are able to connect with our own spiritual identity, through our intuitive faculty, we have to unravel this fear, and release the kidneys, before we can build a relationship with our higher self.

It is our fear which makes it difficult for us to clean out the right hemisphere, to filter away and eliminate (just as the kidneys do in the bloodstream) the negative waste products of our past experience. We fear confronting the memory of the hurt and pain; and we fear taking responsibility for our own misdemeanours and wilful or self-centred actions; we fear the loneliness we seem always to encounter when we dip down into the recesses of our inner world . . . the sense of isolation and rejection . . . the sense of imperfection.

And yet the only way that we can unfurl our intuitive faculty to its full and wondrous capacity, and through it, to become reunited with our higher self, there to participate in the creative unfoldment of understanding, is to release the kidneys to their full resonance and receptivity by draining away their contained tension. When the kidneys free just a little bit, the right hemisphere will begin to loosen, to grow less stiff; fresh rhythms will begin to flow through it and the process of filtering old memories and data, eliminating the dross from these, and re-arranging the positive material that can be reserved for integrating into future growth, can begin.

Each time there is a strong release from the kidneys, there will be a corresponding rush of memories; these may flood the left hemisphere for a time, whilst it works hard to absorb what is relevant, letting go of what isn't. The phase of absorption and elimination is often followed by a rest period before another kidney release allows another group of right hemisphere cells to free and unravel.

This process takes a lot of energy and needs the full attention of the patient. If life circumstances are quite demanding it will take longer and be more arduous and tiring to work through the material as it emerges. An understanding and supportive environment of contacts makes all the difference, no matter what we are tackling! It is always helpful, whether or not this is forthcoming, for the patient to spend the rest phases of the cycle developing some activity that gives refreshment and takes him completely out of the context of his deep growth effort. This can be very physical, such as a sport or physical culture, or it can be a craft like sewing or knitting or carving. Whatever the interest is, it should be followed through, because such activities will enable any emotional residues to be better eliminated as they will be carried down through hands and body and 'pressed out' into the world; but they will also serve to build a core of positive interest which will become a strong foundation for the renewed identity of the patient to spring from.

If, even after the etheric vehicle has become really clear and vibrant, there are still tight resistances in the kidneys and the right hemisphere, it is time to consider deep karmic blocks. It may be helpful for the patient to visit a psychic who can identify the past life experience causing such blocks. This can often help the patient to surrender to the next stage of growth, and of integration of worldly with higher, spiritual identity.

Just as the ear responds to kidney condition, so it will reflect the state of the right hemisphere and the hearing function will gradually change as right hemisphere congestion is released. The area around the eyes will also reveal the state of the kidneys, and so also of the ears: if this is puffy or shadowy you know that the kidneys are dull and thick in their functioning.

It is not possible to 'listen to' the deeper meaning of life unless the kidneys and the right hemisphere are working with clarity. And if we cannot listen to that deeper meaning, we are unable to determine or carry out through our left hemisphere, and the vitality of the liver, our personal role in life. Our life will be shallow and unclear, fuzzy and unable to reflect clearly activity around or within it: distorted ideas, feelings and actions will result.

LIVER AND KIDNEYS FROM THE ANGLE OF THE SPIRITUAL IDENTITY

As we know, life is made up of energy in a state of constant vibration. Although it is present everywhere as frequencies of energy, we are only able to attune ourselves to the frequency that our mechanism is sensitive enough to recognise. If our personality is not very sensitively tuned as yet, we will only be able to respond to very slow, dense vibrations which we call matter, or the body, and we will probably not even recognise this as energy moving at a slow frequency!

However, if we have developed greater sensitivity we will recognise and respond also to fast moving, 'spiritual' frequencies of energy. We will recognise and respond to this everywhere, no matter how overtly 'unspiritual' any situation or circumstance may be.

Spirit is present everywhere; it has no shape or form and is difficult to describe, for this reason. However, it can be focussed through an organ, and when this happens it can clothe itself with form and it can express itself, its will, purpose, design, desire and action, through that form.

The organ that is able to receive the rhythmic vibration or frequency of spirit, and to focus it so that it can express itself in the physical vibratory rhythm of matter, is the Soul. The whole of life is a vibration, or a rhythm, and we are organs through which rhythm plays. The Soul is the organ which focusses the ever so subtle and ethereal rhythm of spirit, enabling us, the individual personalities, to receive it, filtered through the Soul, and transformed so that our personal more crude and dense physical mechanisms may live by it. The spirit gains a personal shape and form and substance through each of our personalities, even though in itself it is impersonal: a rhythm indescribable because without personal or specific features. Each of our personalities is a cell forming a part of the Divine Being, and in each of us, however undeveloped we may be, is reflected the rhythms of spirit, (Mind: air), Soul (emotion: water), and matter (body: earth).

In this context it is the liver, in each of our bodies, which gives form to the spirit. If our liver is not working properly, it will not be possible for us to express our spiritual identity, or to act out our spiritual will in the material world.

This has an interesting bearing on the 'spiritual' healer. Such a one is a transmitter and transformer of extremely high frequency energy; his task is to receive and carry and pass on a frequency of energy which the patient is not yet able to connect with unaided. If the healer is not to suffer physical strain to the point of damage, he will need to take great care to tend his physical liver properly. If the liver is sluggish and clogged with foods and substances which take a lot of effort to detoxify and absorb, he will be limited in his capacity to transmit for others, and will also be unstabilised and weakened through doing this: his liver will function in a thicker, more slow and heavy way on foods which require more work in order to be absorbed.

Just as it is the task of the liver to absorb nourishment from the food given it, so that the body may be supplied with the fuel which enables it to move onward through action, so is it the task of the spirit to absorb information from its experience in the plane of matter (or personalities on Earth), to supply the Whole organism with the fiery intention to move on in its exploration through activity.

It is the kidneys in each of our bodies which correspond with Matter, or Earth: the Mother, as the Spirit is the Father and the Soul, the Son. So:

$$\left\{\begin{matrix}\text{Spirit}\\\text{Liver}\end{matrix}\right\} \text{receives} \left\{\begin{matrix}\text{experience}\\\text{substance}\end{matrix}\right\} \text{from} \left\{\begin{matrix}\text{Matter}\\\text{Kidneys}\end{matrix}\right\} \text{which}$$

stimulates the release of fuel for fiery, outgoing activity from the

$$\left\{\begin{matrix}\text{Spirit}\\\text{Liver}\end{matrix}\right\} \text{which in turn moves the} \left\{\begin{matrix}\text{Body}\\\text{Kidneys}\end{matrix}\right\}$$

into more experience: the result is the spiral of unfolding life wending its way through cycle after cycle, through dark: dawn:light:dusk:phases in each cycle.

When the liver and kidneys are well-balanced and working efficiently, the personality is able to express its will or intention through the physical body. The energy generated by a particular thought can be translated readily into action and so the personality is able to see the tangible product of this thought, and to work upon this and to perfect it. If these two organs are however out of harmony and ailing, this will not be possible. Frustration will result. We will become tight from inability to carry through our ideas. Such frustration results in a general distortion of the flow of force through us; knots and tangles accumulate through the system and cause a damming-up of force in some places and a flowing over into the wrong places elsewhere. Action will distort, and so will thoughts and feelings. The healer will need to try to get these two organs working better so that the patient can begin to work out his life through positive and creative action. Through feeling more connected with and effective in activity on the physical level, he will gradually be able to unravel deeper mental tangles through building a relationship with his own spiritual identity, through prayer or meditation, and a study of the teachings of chosen spiritual thinkers down the ages.

Although we cannot carry through in action spiritual identity and intention if our livers are undermined or clogged, we cannot even respond or connect with that spiritual identity if our kidneys are tight or tremulous. It is fear in particular which inhibits proper kidney functioning, and it is fear then which prevents us from responding to or resonating with the inflowing wave or rhythm from the Soul.

The Base centre (the centre which conditions kidney functioning) is responsible for the distribution of the urge or will to live of the individual personality. If the Base centre retains a pattern of fear experienced during previous lifetimes (almost always the case), the personality will have a certain reluctance about being alive; it will be very difficult for this person wholeheartedly to face and accept and even love the trials, tribulations, dangers and challenges inherent in the condition of human life upon Earth. Such a fear of life itself colours much of society's unconscious efforts and direction: we try so hard to buffer ourselves against all possible difficulties and hardships, physical, emotional, mental and spiritual; we resent our hardships and our trials and strive to build a security in life which prevents them happening. But mostly we simply create barriers between the different parts of ourselves, between ourselves and others, and between ourselves and the planet, the Mother which nourishes, sustains and gives life to our bodies, and the Spirit which inspires us with unfoldment and expanding awareness.

Death is inherent in the very nature of matter; yet the very substance of what has died provides the material for new life. The tree loses its leaves each year; they decay and nourish the following year's growth in the tree. In time the tree itself surrenders its life; it, too, decays or is transformed and concentrated, providing us with fuel for the pursuance of our own life further. A year of experience provides us with learning and new understanding; but in time it seems limited and inappropriate; some part of it fades away but the kernel of truth contained in it remains and becomes the womb from which new wisdom can unfold.

This is a law to which all of life in our world is subjected. If we try to avoid this law we separate ourselves from the source of life itself, and so end by negating our very purpose!

True immortality can only be achieved through becoming at-oned with our spiritual identity and by participating fully in its transformative and creative purpose. This is only possible by welcoming the frequent loss and transformation of the body, or form; but the death of the old form always gives the material and opportunity for new life to unfold through it. Life must always follow death, just as day always follows night, or sunshine the rain, and summer, the winter: it is the law.

Weak kidneys will also mean a reluctant liver (the one who lives will be reluctant to embrace the diversity and richness of the challenge of life!). The kidneys will have to be drained gradually and gently of fear, and then strengthened so that fear may be transformed into courage. Courage results from a good interaction between the kidneys, heart, and liver, and will not only make us able to grapple with our practical lives in a more resilient way, but will also enable us to risk emotional rejection by opening our hearts to intimacy that was earlier shied away from.

If we can achieve and then maintain a balance of these three organs, we can face the challenge of life with courage and with resilience, and can therefore deepen the growth and learning possible from its experience.

In terms of our spiritual functioning, the kidneys usually dominate: if they are poised and tuned to perfection, the liver should be able to radiate out into spiritually-inspired action with ease. However, someone who is very charged with high frequency ('spiritual') force, will inevitably have a liver which is readily unstabilised. If this is not recognised in early life, and habits established which help the liver to cope with its light, fast, sensitive condition, it will fall out of balance and cause the person lots of hassle as the years go by.

The kidneys, then, are the key to our realised spirituality, just as they are at the root of our capacity to anchor or ground ourselves firmly in our worldly personality. But it is the liver which enables us to live out that spirituality, through our earthly personality. The kidney tuning is very, very delicate, but then gives us poise in the world, poised in attunement with our 'highest', most ethereal self, and with our 'lowest', most material self.

CONCLUSION

We have analysed the workings of the liver and kidneys, and their interrelationship, from the point of view of the physical, emotional, mental and spiritual 'bodies'. The activity of these organs at the physical level is the key to their importance at the other levels. If you grasp their role in relationship to the physical body you will gradually find yourself able to see how this corresponds with their role and interrelationship with the other bodies.

When first working with a patient the immediate task facing you will be to get both these organs working with better tone and vitality from the physical point of view. As the physical body begins to respond, the deeper implications of kidney and liver state at the emotional body will become more important; and as this in turn unravels and adjusts, it will be possible to work more directly upon these organs in terms of the mental body. Last but not least, you will find yourself interpreting kidney and liver responses in terms of the spiritual 'body', and working upon them from this point of view.

For some it will not be relevant to work this far, but the responses of the two organs will nevertheless throw helpful interpretative light upon the patient's relationship with his spiritual identity and this will help you to understand better his problem.

The liver conditions our outward self, the personality that we show the world; the state of the liver is often more obvious, and nearer the surface of our being. The kidneys condition our deeper, more intimate and vulnerable self, the aspect we are more reluctant usually to show the world. It will almost always be necessary to adjust the liver before it is possible to begin real work with the kidneys. Sometimes the kidneys will need initially to be soothed a bit before it is worth adjusting the liver, but it will rarely be possible to work at depth with the kidneys, reflecting the deep, fearful side of our natures, until the liver has been re-tuned and adjusted.

Our modern western society encourages the liver to be dominant, and suppresses kidney activity; 'negative' emotions of fear, gentleness, and psychic sensitivity (kidneys) are not given plentiful opportunities for expression, whilst assertiveness, competitiveness, personal drive to success (liver), are admired and rewarded in various obvious and subtle ways. We tend to feel guilty if we are not productively occupied: there is a sense of shame if we spend time doing nothing. Our society is strongly oriented towards having some goal to work towards and these goals are usually to do with gain of a material or status kind. We are thought a bit odd, and kept at a distance if we take time to 'listen to God'. This means that people who are born with a dominant kidney rhythm and who therefore are drawn towards everything that resonates with the inward, deeper self that leads eventually into the depths of the essence of the Spirit of life, will often experience much hardship and pain as their life-journey unfolds.

Many will suppress their kidney sensitivity and force their liver rhythm to be stronger. This may work in a worldly sense but will cause much confusion and crossed wires at a deeper level.

The tendency in our society to encourage pushy livers is present in all corners of our life now: we feed ourself foods and drinks which stimulate the liver to more fieriness and weaken the kidneys by overloading the bloodstream with toxins. Weak kidneys means a tendency to be easily infected with weak emotions: fear and insecurity become even stronger in the roots of our being; and our society, already thriving so much on paranoia, does so even more. The separation of groups within the social structure grows more extreme: the Haves have even more and the Have Nots have even less, whilst mediators (social workers) appointed by the Haves make attempts in the context of the Haves' thought patterns and ethics to improve matters, yet nothing seems to change . . . because mostly the Haves are not prepared to question deeply enough the roots of the problem as this would mean questioning their own deeper attitudes.

The Haves are too busy pushing their livers to deal with the superficial and outward state of affairs (the symptoms) to be able to sink down into a state of listening receptivity to their kidney rhythm; they cannot then attune themselves to the depths or essence of themselves or of others; they cannot hear the rhythm emanating from the Spirit of life, and so they cannot grasp the deeper intention or Plan underlying the outward pattern of life.

Sickness and pain force us to confront the deeper realities of life, and to question our style of participation in it. They force us when we can no longer hold back the symptoms, to consider the causes . . . we begin then to connect with the part of ourselves reflected in the kidneys.

It is not safe for us to recognise too clearly our deeper processes until we feel stronger and more stable, more agile and alert and poised, in the part of ourselves which must deal with the ever-changing, unpredictable and often challenging world around us. When we feel more confident and relaxed at work, in social situations and in domestic problems, then we are ready to get to grips with the contents of our deeper psyche.

Always work mostly through these organs from the physical point of view. In other words, be very tentative about stimulating the Heart centre, or stirring up the head area: aim always to drain tensions away down through the body; only very occasionally, when you feel in the whole of yourself that it is appropriate, work directly upon the Heart centre or the head.

This means that you will not frequently use the Bridge or the High Blood Pressure releases, although you know that there will be times when these releases are the right ones to use.

Any tension or blocks released in the etheric vehicle will stimulate corresponding areas in the physical body to throw off tension. This tension must be drained away or it will cause its own energy-distribution problems. This draining is done through the kidneys and liver at the physical level, so keep referring back to the condition here, assessing and adjusting it. What is happening at the physical level is a key to what is happening at the subtler levels. But the physical body is the vehicle for the expression of the spiritual identity, so it is essential to tune it well if it is to perform this task. The emotional, mental and spiritual bodies pass their condition down through the physical; if tensions and tangles at these subtle levels are not quickly freed down through the physical body, and 'earthed' or grounded, they will clog and inhibit the physical functioning and in time physical tensions themselves will seep back into the emotional and mental levels, crystallising and intensifying existing problems in these areas.

The result is a vicious cycle which can be difficult to break. The thing to remember is that in essence life is energy in constant movement. It must flow; when flow is inhibited or prevented, distortion and disease result. Your main aim as a healer is to make it possible once more for energy to flow, by identifying knots and tangles where it is snarling up, and teasing these gently out.

The whole problem is about balance and flow: flow needs to take place between the different parts, or vibratory rates, of ourselves and this flow needs to be in balance, or harmony.

Similarly, throughout the whole of society, through all its different parts, or vibratory rates, there needs to be flow in balance; and between human life, individual and group, and the different parts, or vibratory rates, of planetary life, there needs to be flow in balance and harmony. In seeking to bring about a better harmony of flow in the interaction of the kidneys and the liver in the individual we work bit by bit towards a better harmony of flow in the whole planet.

THE GREAT INVOCATION

From the point of Light within the mind of God
Let Light stream forth into the minds of men
Let Light descend on Earth.

From the point of Love within the heart of God
Let Love stream forth into the hearts of men
May Christ return to Earth.

From the centre where the Will of God is known
Let purpose guide the little wills of men
The purpose which the masters know and serve.

From the centre which we call the Race of men
Let the Plan of Love and Light work out
And may it seal the door where evil dwells.

Let Light and Love and Power
Restore the Plan on Earth.

Invocation

10. Diet for Detoxification and Rejuvenation of the Liver and Kidneys

Part of the work of the liver is to alter the composition of incoming food substances so that they can be properly made use of by the body, or converted into energy which we burn as fuel. When the liver functioning breaks down it is unable to produce the chemical combinations needed in the right proportions. This means that all the other workings of the body suffer.

The main work of the kidneys is to filter the bloodstream of impurities so that it is clear and free from 'silt'. When they get clogged and overloaded they cannot carry out this filtering in an efficient way so the impurities seep back into the cell tissue where they continue to hamper proper cell activity until the kidneys operate properly once more.

The intestines mix food and digestive juices thoroughly with a massage-like movement and also absorb through their walls many nourishing substances released as a result.

Most people lack optimum activity of both liver, kidneys and intestines, resulting in an inability to absorb the full nutritive value of food, over-production of toxic by-products (from poor metabolism), and the inability to filter out of the bloodstream these toxins which are then carried to muscles, organs and brain and nervous system, inhibiting their good activity.

When the work of the liver, kidneys and intestines is hindered for whatever reason (disease, heredity, poor diet, etc), the cells which form them become steadily more clogged and blocked with substances that should be eliminated from the body. The organs become more and more sluggish, and more and more silted up and the whole body in turn functions with less and less vitality and becomes more susceptible to illness. To restore these organs to their proper vitality, they must first be cleaned of the build-up of 'silt' within their cell structure. As the cleaning is carried out they will be enabled to absorb the elements they need from the food given them and this in turn will gradually enable them to recapture better tone and working capacity.

If we maintain our capacity to absorb and eliminate in good working order we are less susceptible to the ageing process as well as being less likely to fall sick.

The diet described here has the power to cleanse the cell tissue at an ever deeper and deeper level, and to gently carry away the rubbish released through the cleansing process. It is also a diet extremely rich in all the minerals, vitamins, proteins, lipids (Essential Fatty Acids) and carbohydrates needed for the body to radiate good health. What is more, because it is based on the plant kingdom, it is very low in metal and chemical toxins which accumulate and become more 'fixed' the higher we move up the food chain. It is a diet which is very easy to digest, so although it gives lots of energy, it requires very little for its metabolism. A diet containing meat is rich in substances of a toxic nature which our bodies were not designed to make use of. This is because of the wide use of antibiotics, chemical fertilisers, pesticides, which quickly build up and remain in animal cell tissue.

Unfortunately even fish comes into this category now because our oceans have become the dumping ground for much land waste. Dairy products are also now high in toxins for the same reasons: milk is an extremely absorbant substance which soaks up and passes on to us radioactivity and other pollutants. These substances are also present in the products made from milk and cream.

Regardless of whether you prefer not to eat animal products for moral reasons, it is much easier to achieve and maintain good body functioning if these are eliminated.

However, it seems that the digestive systems of some people cannot cope with a diet high in grain and for them the approach described here would not be suitable. In any case it would be wise for anyone shifting to this way of eating to do so gradually in order to give the body time to get used to it without too much shock.

It is a very low cost diet, and very little equipment is needed. It will probably seem tasteless at first but in time, when the body has adjusted and is becoming more vital, will be found very satisfying even to the tastebuds.

It can be used as a temporary measure, simply to clean the

body. To do this thoroughly could take about six months. Some other, more varied diet could be returned to after that time, the cleansing diet used once more from time to time for a couple of weeks when needed. It can also be taken on as a stable, permanent way of eating, breaking it only from time to time for social occasions. It is very useful used like this for people with allergies, hypoglycaemia, candida, liver disease, etc.

You need sprouting trays, and a pressure cooker greatly reduces cooking time. If you live in an urban area it is highly advisable to use a water filter. These are available at health food stores and don't cost much.

The diet is based upon rotating all foods. This means that you eat the same food only for one day in every four. First determine which staple carbohydrates suit you best. For example, rice, buckwheat, millet and oats would give you a four day rotation of your staple food which would also assure an intake of plentiful minerals, B vitamins, proteins, carbohydrates and lipids. Other staples are barley, rye, potatoes, wheat, maize. But these last cause digestive problems for many people.

Cook a full pan of your staple food and use that as the basis of each meal. What is not eaten straightaway can be covered in a clean dish in the fridge and used according to need until it is finished.

For protein use the pulses. Experiment until you find the ones you like the best. It is best to sprout most pulses before using as the constituents are then converted into a form more easily digested by the body, and also many more vitamins and minerals are formed in the young sprout which grows from each bean.

The best beans to sprout are mung, chickpeas, lentils and aduki, and you may like to use lima, haricot and red kidney beans unsprouted for a change. If using beans unsprouted they must be soaked overnight, the water discarded, then boiled fast in fresh water for 10 minutes before simmering for about forty minutes or until tender. A pressure cooker makes cooking much quicker. Sprouted beans are more digestible and less windy if steamed for a minute or two before eating.

You should also sprout enough alfalfa and fenugreek seeds to eat these raw with meals every few days. These have a wonderfully high vitamin and mineral content and are also a digestive aid. Sunflower seeds sprouted are a good variation on beans as a source of high protein. Almonds can also be used and need no sprouting. Otherwise it is best to keep seed and nut consumption to a minimum, for two reasons:

a. They have a high oil and protein content which means that the liver has to work very hard to metabolise them.
b. The oils they contain are almost always rancid by the time they reach the shelf, making them toxic and thereby giving the liver extra work.

However, it is worth knowing that pumpkin seeds have a high zinc content (a mineral essential to the digestive functioning), and sesame seeds are high in calcium.

If you are using this diet in order to detoxify and deep-cleanse your liver, you will need, nevertheless, to use all nuts and seeds in extreme moderation.

Of the vegetables, emphasise the dark green curly-leafed kind, carrots and onions; but use vegetables also in moderation unless you can obtain organically grown ones. This is because vegetables, like fruit, are mostly coated with pesticides, and forced to grow in nutrient-depleted soil with the false aid of chemical fertilisers. Our bodies are not designed to digest these chemical and toxic agents. Also in cities vegetables collect pollutants from the air and the streets.

Fruits too suffer the above abuses. They are also full of water and sugar (fructose). This makes them suitable in hot climates, where the body needs to be cooled down. But in Ireland and cold or damp climates the body needs foods which supply heat and substance so that it can generate the energy to keep moving and maintain a good body temperature.

Salads have a similar effect of cooling the body and raw vegetables can be difficult for a weak liver to digest. Fruits and salads should be reserved for special occasions and really hot weather.

If you keep a daily supply of beansprouts you have the freshest possible vegetables at your fingertips.

Your basic meals will consist of, for example:

Day 1: rice, chopped alfalfa sprouts, steamed mung beans
Day 2: porridge from oatmeal, raw sunflower seeds sprouted; oatmeal biscuits (mix oatmeal with cumin or aniseed and water to a stiff dough, pat into baking tray and bake in a moderate oven until lightly browned); onion and kuzu soup (finely chop 1 onion and put into pan with 1 tsp

kuzu and 1 tsp agar-agar powder; bring to the boil stirring all the time; simmer gently for 1 minute)

Day 3: millet, lima beans cooked until soft, with coriander and cumin, thin soup with leeks and curly kale and fenugreek seeds

Day 4: buckwheat, sprouted chickpeas steamed with fresh thyme, chopped cress

Begin once more with rice, but vary your vegetable and protein (sprouted pulse) from the selection which agrees with you best. The thing to remember is to eat as much as your appetite requires of the staple grain, adding only about one third of the total meal quantity of sprouted pulse (which is your combined protein and fresh vegetable source). You may safely be able to use alfalfa sprouts more frequently than once in four days, once in a while eating none for a week or two, perhaps while you have access to organic vegetables.

All grains can be used as flours, meaning that you can bake them into breads and biscuits for a change of texture. However, they are not so kind or so cleansing to the intestines in this form and so should be seen as a treat. Also flours bought in shops are often not too fresh as they have a slow turnover and so you should make your own, using an electric coffee grinder.

Never eat fried or sauteed foods. However you can add a few drops of olive, sesame or vitamin E oil, marine fish or Evening Primrose oil to your meal each day. The last three are available in gelatine capsule form. Take a sharp knife and open the capsule, pouring the oil onto your food.

It is an excellent idea to take spirulina (1,000–3,000mg daily) as a supplement with this or indeed any diet. It has a high B12 content which protects non-meat eaters from poor iron absorption and lack. But it also contains all the amino acids, lots of vitamin A (for the immune system), calcium, iron, iodine (for good thyroid functioning) and numerous other vitamins and minerals. It is an algae found in high altitude lakes, gathered, dried and compressed into tablet form. This makes it an organic and very non-tampered-with food supplement. If you have problems with allergies you should also take a little zinc each day (three 10mg tablets on an empty stomach).

It is also very important to make sure you are getting enough iodine, either from seaweeds in your meals, or sprinkling a little kombu powder onto your food. The high speed of modern life demands a fast metabolism and this means the thyroid needs help . . . it cannot work efficiently without plenty of iodine. Also adequate iodine helps the body to not absorb some radioactive toxicity.

Your food may seem very bland until you grow accustomed to this way of eating. You can ease this problem by using herbs and seeds for flavouring. Cumin, coriander, aniseed and caraway can be added to grains during cooking to both flavour and aid digestion. Rosemary and thyme are good chopped and added to sprouted pulses. Onions, garlic, and shallots can also be used and help draw toxins from the body.

Herb teas drunk between meals will ease away any feelings of uncertainty or loss in your tummy: nettle, sage, elderflower, yarrow, ginger, rosemary and vervain for the lymphatic system (aids cleansing) and the nervous system, liver and digestion and to ease any side effects of your body's removal of toxins.

Lemon balm, passion flowers, lavender and rosemary will soothe headaches and nervousness and help the sleep to be sound.

Liquorice tea (take three liquorice roots, chop and split and simmer in 1 pt of water for 5 minutes; reuse the same roots until flavourless) will help female hormonal congestion and sugar balance if you have hypoglycaemia or sugar cravings.

A mixture of kuzu, agar-agar and slippery elm powder (1 tsp of each) simmered gently for a short time in 1 pt of water will soothe and draw toxins from the length of the digestive tract, nourishing at the same time.

The high grain fibre content of this diet draws into itself impurities from the digestive tract absorbing and then eliminating these in the faeces. It is this highly absorptive property of the grains which enables the diet to cleanse at such a deep level. It is as though the inner body is being gently scrubbed and massaged. Linusit Gold from health food stores will also help this inner cleansing, but also is rich in Essential Fatty Acids which aid the metabolism of carbohydrates, brain, thyroid and skin condition. Two to four teaspooonsful daily is all that is needed.

The kuzu, agar-agar and slippery elm mixture helps this process even further.

Two or three times a week make a soup of cooked lima or other beans, chopped potato, carrot, parsnip, onion, curly kale, rosemary and bay leaves, and sprinkle chopped parsley over the top. Eat this along with your grain staple. If you don't have candida, or if this is now under control, you can add miso to this soup to enrich it further.

Use kombu powder to replace salt. This is a powdered seaweed and so is very high in iodine which your thyroid needs in order to balance your metabolism better. But don't overdo it as it has a high salt content which may disturb your liver.

WITHDRAWAL SYMPTOMS AND CRAVINGS

This is quite an extreme diet for most people and it is a good idea to ease into it gently. Otherwise your body is likely to experience shock, which could be dramatic and even scary and put you off carrying the diet through to the point where you experience its benefits. This is particularly true as most people will experience withdrawal symptoms and cravings whilst the liver and kidneys adjust and throw out poisons from the body. It is advisable to have help from a healer, acupuncturist, homoeopath, reflexologist or massage therapist to cope with this detoxification period.

Experiment with your own ability to adjust. First use this diet one day in each week. When you have got used to the bland flavours and the changed sensations in your tummy, try two days each week. Carry on like this until you can eat this way for a whole week. After a time follow the diet every other week, then two weeks on and one week off. In this way gradually reach the point where this is your basic mode of eating except for the occasional treat – perhaps once a week on a social occasion.

Withdrawal symptoms will vary from person to person but are always the result of the liver achieving the tone to release old toxins into the bloodstream, to be carried to the kidneys for filtering out and eliminating. They can go on for a long time because the liver will at first only have the strength to release the toxins nearest itself: the cells of the liver itself. The process will go in cycles: a phase of toxic release followed by a time when both liver and cleaner cells rest. Then the liver and these cells will be able to make use of their new state – they will have improved tone, and cells further away will be enabled to release their toxic burden. This same principle applies to the kidneys, which will first need to clean the cells which form its own filtering system. The kidneys have a double workload as they have not only to clean their own cell structure, but at the same time to filter and eliminate the extra waste content carried to them in the blood from the liver: the liver scrubs its cells clean and tips the refuse into the bloodstream for the kidneys to filter away.

This is really the cause of the withdrawal symptoms experienced during any cleansing diet. The kidneys are given an extra workload which they are often too weak to cope with in a vital way. The use of herb teas which strengthen kidney functioning is of enormous use here. The best are borage, nettle, sage, cleavers and dandelion. These are all rich in minerals which heal and revitalise kidney cells. As the kidneys improve, there will be a better flow of adrenalin and this will enable the dieter to exercise the body more. If you can get out into fresh clean air and exercise strongly enough to cause you to breathe more deeply and freely, you will fill your bloodstream with oxygen which will stimulate much better vitality of all cells and tissues, resulting in your whole body working with more dynamism. The cleansing process will move more rapidly and smoothly as a result.

All withdrawal symptoms will be eased through fresh air exercise bringing a better intake of oxygen.

The commonest withdrawal symptoms are headaches, skin rashes of all kinds, intermittent aches and pains in joints, diarrhoea, bouts of lethargy and sleep disturbance. Try to allow some time each day which is completely in your own control, and use this to deal with your withdrawal symptoms, through fresh air exercise if this is appropriate, through receiving healing massage treatment, or through rest with the help of a deep relaxation and stress release tape. Your aim in combating withdrawal symptoms is to stimulate your metabolism with deep oxygenation, or to release stress and tension build-up through deep rest; and using the herb teas mentioned to balance and strengthen kidney functioning. If possible do not use these herbs in teabag form. Their potency is much greater if used whole and they are mostly available now in packets from a good health food store. Otherwise write to Baldwin & Co., 173–174 Walworth Road, London SE17, for a catalogue.

Mental withdrawal symptoms will often accompany physical ones and the way to deal with these is the same. It is also very helpful however to have someone near to you who understands the principle of what you are trying to do and is able to listen to you talk about your problems in a non-judgmental way. The mental symptoms will include a sense of panic, anxiety, depression, pending doom, nervous self-doubt, general negativity and even perceptual distortions. You need to be able to voice these, and to be able to trust that the person you are voicing them to is able to reassure and soothe and encourage you and not drag you off to a psycho-analyst. To go for long walks near greenery or the sea, talking with a friend as you walk, is extremely beneficial.

Cravings result from a disturbed liver chemistry. Chemical chain reactions in the liver become unbalanced from (for example) drug use, over reliance on sugar or sugar products, additives in food. The natural functioning of the liver is undermined and it becomes weak and lazy and dependent upon the very substance that is undermining it. This is when we crave certain foodstuffs. Cravings are usually for sugars, proteins and fats, and will be worst when the liver is weakest. To help to heal cravings it is once more essential to have control over some of the hours in each day. Use these for deep relaxation, massage therapy, or fresh air oxygenation, whichever is important. But it can also be very helpful to have some thing that you can freely chew upon without further disturbing your liver. Rice cakes are good for this. Although they lack flavour, they need chewing and so satisfy the restless need of the jaw and at the same time result in a flow of digestive juices which helps the system further down the digestive tract to fulfil its task. Oatcakes can also be useful in this way, but be wary because these often contain salt and heavy oils which undermine liver activity. Sipping Perrier water with a few drops of Rescue Remedy added is also helpful. Perrier springs from the earth already carbonated and contains very healing combinations of minerals.

Eating some fruit occasionally can also ease cravings. Kiwi, apples and grapefruits or tangerines are good because of their high vitamin C content. Nevertheless they should be taken with care in a cool climate as they have a chilling and wind-producing effect upon the liver.

Some people may think this diet would be fattening because of its high carbohydrate content. The opposite is true. Carbohydrate only creates fat deposits when combined with fats and sugars or too large a proportion of protein. When eaten as described here it will enable pounds of unwanted, weighty and waste-laden flesh to melt effortlessly away. The loss is effortless because there is no hunger. The body may find itself receiving nourishment it has needed for the first time in its life. It is important when using this diet to eat only when hungry and to eat only as much as the body demands. In this way the body organs can regulate themselves. If you eat more at one sitting than you have digestive juices to cope with you will be overloading your system with extra work; however, if you miss meals when your body asks for food, you will be putting a strain on already weakened organs. Modern city life makes it difficult to follow the needs of our bodies but it is possible to find ways. For instance, take a lunchbox of your day's grain and sprouted pulse with you so that if necessary you can eat your chosen diet no matter where you are. If you feel embarrassed by your friends' comments say you feel like some fresh air and take your meal out to the park to eat, or to your car if it is wet, or stay in the office when the others go to the canteen. If necessary, make some light-hearted comment about your unusual diet if you have to remain in company. If we really want to do something there is usually a way of doing it.

SUMMARY OF DETOXIFICATION DIET

Purpose of the diet:

a. To detoxify liver and kidneys and eventually the whole body.
b. To enable these organs to gain new tone and vitality so they better absorb nourishment, eliminate waste products and maintain an efficient immune system as a natural defense against disease.
c. To free the body of damage or disease to the liver from addictions, immune system problems like ME, candida, etc. Because the liver and kidneys are at the root of all physical workings of the body, helping them to work better will help very many health problems including skin problems, nervous problems and digestive problems, even though in serious cases professional help should always be sought.
d. To experience bright eyes, clear skin, a wide awake mind, new spring in the body, less sickness and fresh richness of life.

Principle:

a. To use foods very close to their natural state, and low in toxic fertilisers, pesticides and additives.
b. To use foods which require little energy for their absorption, yet supply steady energy.
c. To rotate all foods on a four or more day basis so the body has variety of nutrients, yet rests regularly from all foods.

Foods used:

a. Staple carbohydrate: e.g. rice, millet, oats, buckwheat, rye, maize, potatoes.
b. Protein: sprouted pulses (e.g. mung, chickpea, aduki, lentils), sprouted seeds (e.g. sunflowers, almonds, pumpkins), some unsprouted pulses (e.g. aduki, lima, split peas, red lentils, haricot).
c. Vegetable: onions, garlic, shallots, leeks, carrots, parsnips, curly kale, broccoli, parsley, cress, spring onion, green lettuce, avocado (rarely); sprouted pulses and seeds; sprouted alfalfa and fenugreek; seaweeds (ask in health food stores). Emphasise dark green leafy vegetables for plenty of vitamin C: curly kale, broccoli, parsley, cress and spring onion or chives.
d. Herbs and condiments: cumin, coriander, aniseed, ginger, fresh thyme and rosemary, kombu powder.
e. Drinks: nettle, borage, vervain, ginger, liquorice, kuzu mixed with agar-agar and slippery elm, Perrier, rescue remedy. Filtered water.
f. Use 1 tsp olive oil or sesame oil, 500mg Evening Primrose oil or Marine oil or Glanolin, or 100iu vitamin E oil, and 2 tsps Linusit Gold, with two meals in the day. Or use all of these at different times to ensure a varied intake of Essential Fatty Acids.

All foods should be steamed: vegetables lightly, unsprouted pulses and grains according to their type (see cookbook). Eat a combination of these foods at each meal (drinks are better taken between meals) and eat small amounts frequently until your body is stronger. The herbs used as teas will help to detoxify the kidneys and tone the liver. The staple portion of each meal should fill ⅔ of your plate, the remaining ⅓ being made up of vegetables and proteins.

Cravings and withdrawal symptoms:

a. Get regular help in detoxification from aromatherapy, acupuncture, homoeopath, counsellor or healer.
b. Maintain a regular exercise and relaxation daily plan including walking by the sea or amongst greenery, swimming, jogging, dance or other indoor activities that increase your depth of breathing and appeal to you. Use deep relaxation

tape and soothing music. Assert full control over your free time and you can use relaxation or de-stressing work on yourself at times when you are feeling the strain of your de-toxification.

Highly recommended is a book called *Nature's Foods* by Peter Deadman and Karen Betteridge, published by Rider & Co., 3 Fitzroy Square, London, W1. It is beautifully produced and gives background notes on most foods, ideas for different occasions, how to grow sprouts, etc.

Take Spirulina, 1,000–3,000mg daily, in divided doses and with food; and zinc gluconate, three 10mg tablets first thing in the morning, on an empty stomach.

11. The Relationship with the Soul

The personality is made up of three vibratory rhythms: the mind (mental body), the emotions (emotional body), and the physical body. Each of these three rhythms is itself made up of two rhythms, an active and a receptive rhythm, or an inner and an outer rhythm. The inner, receptive rhythm responds to that which comes from within, and is not visible to the physical senses; the outer, active rhythm makes it possible for the individual personality to follow its own chosen direction and goal in the world.

Each pair of rhythms, mental, emotional and physical, is more delicate and sensitive than the one before it: the physical is the slowest, heaviest rhythm; the emotional is more subtle than this, and the mental is more subtle again.

These three pairs of vibratory rhythm flow through the centres in the personality and give that personality its individual nature. The Soul is also made up of three vibratory rhythms, called the Knowledge petals, the Love-Wisdom petals, and the Sacrifice petals.

The personality first approaches the Soul through the mind. We listen to the inner, receptive rhythm of the mind and through turning this towards the Soul (upwards and inwards) it gradually learns to hear the rhythm of the Knowledge petals of the Soul, with which it already has a strong affinity, both Knowledge and mind being vibrations within the vibratory rhythm of Manas (Spiritual Triad).

When the Knowledge petals and the mind are readily harmonised, the emotional body is able to harmonise its rhythm with the middle ring of petals in the lotus of the Soul: the petals of Love-Wisdom. The whole personality resonates more strongly with the vibration of the Soul; this transforms it and the transformation will be felt within the individual and also by those with whom he is associated.

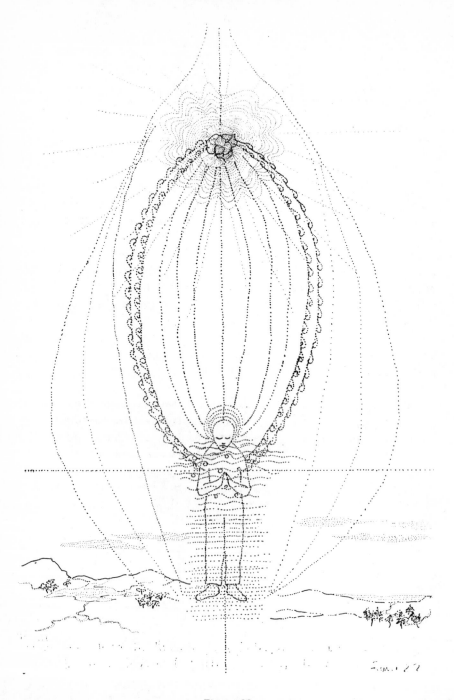

Figure 22

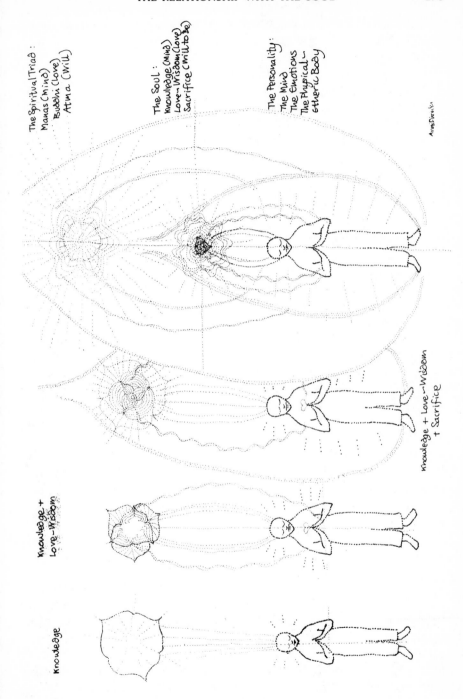

The Spiritual (Triad):
Manas (Mind)
Buddhi (Love)
Atma (Will)

The Soul:
Knowledge (Mind)
Love–Wisdom (Love)
Sacrifice (Will to Be)

The Personality:
The Mind
The Emotions
The Physical–
etheric Body

Knowledge + Love–Wisdom
+ Sacrifice

Knowledge +
Love–Wisdom

Knowledge

Figure 23

Next, the rhythm of the physical-etheric body is absorbed into the central ring of petals, whose quality is Sacrifice, and the personality rhythm becomes more centred, more integrated, yet simultaneously more orientated towards some form of service.

The cage of the personality, enclosing turmoil, unhappiness and bewilderment, is transformed into an auric envelope in the shape of a spiritual flame which burns out coarse matter at physical, emotional and mental levels, building in its place substance delicate of hue, and note and touch, yet intense with essential livingness. This flame burns like a sword through the personality in response to the Soul, devouring all obstacles, hindrances and dross, illuminating the way ahead, and releasing the essential life force imprisoned in the personality, to new growth and flowering.

When the orientation is of personality to world, it is only possible to be aware of bodily sensations (physical), desires for love-gratification (emotional) and attitudes and thought reactions (mental). When orientation is as a Soul-infused personality, awareness grows of Knowledge (free from reactions), present everywhere, a force which can be mobilised and acted upon for the good of the whole; of Love-Wisdom, unconditional, the right of each of us to be bathed in the community of the One Life, also a force to be mobilised and acted upon for the good of the whole; and of Sacrifice: the immortality of the Spirit, which lives and moves and has its Being through the manifest world in space and time, discarding forms and bodies that have outgrown its capacity for self-discovery, and flowing in and out of new forms and bodies, effervescent with the joy of self-discovery, the eternal continuity of the Spirit, a force which lends power and dynamism to our individual lives in all places and at all times.

INTRODUCTION

When we work as healers, our hands are magnetically drawing away from the patient the bands of tension which inhibit a balanced distribution of the life-force; at the same time, our minds are held poised in attunement with the Soul. This electrical activity of the attuned mind and Soul stimulates a richer flow of life-force to the patient and it is this flow of life-force which determines the unfoldment of better health in that person.

If the healer neglects his relationship with the Soul, and

instead uses his mind to seek to carry energy into the patient, this energy will flow from his own personality and will or desire. He will find the healing work very exhausting and he will also transmit any imbalance in himself to the patient: energy can only flow along open pathways and if the healer has blocks or restrained areas (and who amongst us does not!), the energy will flow through and from him only in the pattern of these blocks. He may indeed bring about some healing in his patient, but it will only be in accordance with the pattern of his own development. He will also feel weakened by the healing work because he is seeking to use his own life force to help his patient.

When working from the level of the Soul one is simply a channel, a pathway through which energy can find its way from one place to another. The healing will still be limited by the development of the healer's relationship with the Soul, but if the healer is sincerely dedicated to working at unfolding this relationship and following it through, it will steadily blossom and become richer, more tangible and real. The healer will find his ability to heal and his understanding of the patient's problem will blossom and enrich accordingly. The relationship with the Soul will be nourished and enhanced by the healing work that we as healers offer ourselves for. Also, our exposure to the vibration of the Soul, whilst working as healers, will gently adjust and purify and revitalise our own inner energy distribution even as we open ourselves as channels for the need of our patient.

The distinction resides in the fact that the personality is an expression of our personal self, with all its lopsidedness and limitation; the Soul, however, is impersonal, and an expression of the essential qualities of the Divine Life, and of the Whole. When working from our personality, no matter how good the technique used, we can only achieve a result conditioned by that personality; when, however, we work from the Soul, our personality limitations are by-passed (according to the degree of development of our relationship with the Soul), and the quality of the Soul is transmitted to the patient (and therefore a source of energy infinitely more encompassing, expressive of the Whole, and free from personal conditions). This quality gently melts away knots and tangles in the patient, and enables the source of all life to flow with greater fullness throughout that person. The only effort made by the personality is of holding itself focussed in alignment with the Soul, and receptive to its vibratory rhythm.

If we are to build a relationship with the Soul we need to know something about it: what it is and how it works.

First, we must hold in our minds that all of life is energy in vibratory activity. The vibrations move always, but their frequency and wavelengths vary. They produce rhythm. The healer is one who is sensitive enough to become aware of and resonate with, exquisitely subtle and refined rhythms. These ever so subtle rhythms emanate from the Soul and from beyond the Soul. But before we can attune ourselves to rhythms coming from an even more refined source than the Soul – the Spiritual Triad – we have to become so at one with the Soul that its rhythm and our own are indistinguishable.

The Soul is an organ formed simply of concentrated or focussed wavelengths of vibrating energy: when many wavelengths cross each other and come together, a nucleus is formed which has its own qualities and characteristics. It does not become separate from the whole field of energy, it is simply distinguishable within that field because of the specific qualities it then expresses.

The senses of hearing, sight, touch, etc, can perceive this Soul organ, but only once they have developed to a high degree of sensitivity.

The Soul, once it has formed from overlapping wavelengths, has the capacity to radiate or transmit energy. What it does is to focus the wavelengths emitted by the spiritual Triad so they can be received by the individual personality at the human level.

The healer, when seeking to be an agent for spiritual healing, must train his own personality mechanism to resonate perfectly with the rhythm of force emanating from the Soul. The personality is really an instrument, or organ, just as the Soul is, for the transmission of energy, but it needs to be tuned just right in order to carry out this transmission and radiation without distortion or interference from itself. The fine tuning enables the personality mechanism to hear or pick up, to become one with and attuned to, and then to transmit or radiate, the very subtle rhythm of the Soul.

The two concepts that we need to hold in our mind are: an arena, or field, consisting of rhythm, and organs situated in this arena of rhythm. The rhythm plays through the organ: the organ has the capacity to pick up and redistribute the rhythm. The more finely it is tuned the more able it is to pick up the subtler rhythms and to redistribute these.

The person who wishes to work as a spiritual healer learns how to tune himself, as the organ or instrument, to the rhythm of the Soul, and how to redistribute, radiate and transmit this rhythm for others.

We become skilled at tuning our personality organ to receive and transmit spiritual rhythms or wavelengths of energy by unfolding our relationship with the Soul.

STRUCTURE OF THE PERSONALITY AND OF THE SOUL

Within each of us can be found three different kinds of activity: we have a physical body, an emotional or feeling nature, and a mental or thinking capacity. Each of these kinds of activity is in essence a vibratory rhythm, and the three are co-ordinated and integrated by a fourth, which we call the spiritual aspect. The spiritual aspect is often quite a vague and uncertain quality; through it we approach the Soul; however faint our first contact may be, it becomes the first rung in the ladder we steadily build so that we may come closer and closer to the reality of that Soul. As we draw nearer to it, our spiritual aspect and identity become more visible and more clearly defined.

The Soul also is made up of three aspects, each one being in essence the same as each aspect of the personality. The Soul is envisaged as a lotus made up of three rows of petals, an outer, a middle and an inner row. The outer row of petals are called the Knowledge petals. Their vibratory rhythm is in essence exactly that of the mind, or mental aspect of the personality. But although the rhythm of the mind is essentially that of the knowledge petals of the Soul, outwardly it is clothed with a denser, thicker, more crude rhythm that veils the inner rhythm from being readily tangible.

This means that to hear the rhythm of the Knowledge petals of the Soul we have only to listen to the rhythm of the essence of our own minds. But unfortunately it is not so easy, as our minds are more adept at listening to what is outside themselves and obvious: the clatter of the world and the business of day-to-day activity! To hear the rhythm emanating from these outermost petals of the Soul body we have to learn to tune out all that attracts our interest outside of ourselves and instead listen with the inner ear only to the pulse of our inner being.

The second aspect of the Soul is also made up of three petals and these are called the Love petals. These petals vibrate in essence to the same rhythm as the emotional or feeling aspect of the personality, yet, as with the mental aspect and the knowledge petals, it is outwardly clothed with a more crude or thick and tangible rhythm. If we can be sensitive to the essential rhythm emanating from our emotional lives we can also sense the rhythm emanating from and expressed by the Love petals of the Soul.

The Love petals of the Soul express a quality that is more delicate, more sensitive still, than the Knowledge petals. However, in the structure of the personality, the outward expression of the emotions (processed and distributed through the Solar Plexus centre) is less sensitive than the inner expression of the mind.

The third aspect of the Soul is comprised of the three petals of Sacrifice. This is the innermost row of petals and it expresses a rhythm which is in essence the same as that of the etheric body of the personality, upon which the physical is built. The rhythm emanating from the physical body is the most obvious and tangible in our whole personality, but if we can tune out its outward, demanding note, we become able to hear its other, etheric rhythm, at the essence of itself, and through this we can attune ourselves in turn with the Sacrifice petals at the heart of the Lotus of the Soul.

As with the emotional and the mental aspects of the personality, so with the physical-etheric: although the outer vibration of this is denser and more crude and obvious than that of the emotional and the mental, its inner rhythm is even more subtle and more delicate than the inner rhythms of the emotional and the mental, even though at the Soul level the Sacrifice petals emanate a vibration altogether more refined than the Love and Knoweldge petals.

It is not possible for the personality to attune itself to the rhythm of the Spiritual Triad until it has become able to hear and respond to the note emanating from the Sacrifice petals; this cannot take place until the personality is completely at-oned in rhythm with the Love and the Knowledge petals.

This is the structure of the Soul. The relationship of the personality with the Soul develops according to this structure.

UNFOLDING THE RELATIONSHIP WITH THE SOUL

When we begin to seek contact with our Soul we reach out with our minds for some point we can recognise or identify as a key to the peace and nourishment we have been promised by spiritual teachers and sages down through the ages. When we look for help in our human suffering, or cry out for an end to our pain, or at least for some ray or sign of hope or understanding, we are told to look inwards to our consciences and to God. Usually in desperation and at the end of our tether, ready to try anything once anyway, we do look inward, searching through the darkness of our private confusion for some glimmer of light to point the way.

There are a few classical ways whereby we approach our inner selves, and seek audience with the Divine. Prayer and meditation are the best known.

We find a place that is as quiet as we can make it, knowing that the sounds of the hectic activity of the day-to-day world will distract our minds outwards and away from our aim. If we can find such a place, we make sure that we will be free from interruption for quite a while by taking the phone off the hook and putting a 'Don't Disturb' sign on the door. We get ourselves into a position that is upright yet without strain and we first of all give our attention to our bodily sensations. We listen to our breath and allow it to become even and quiet and unstrained; we scan our limbs and torso for stiffness or tension and instruct this to relax and unwind when we identify it, sometimes tensing and untensing groups of muscles, or giving a little wriggle or shake to chase tension away.

Next we do the same with our feelings, looking for any emotional preoccupation or resistance. And lastly we examine our mental activity. We do this by just watching our thoughts. When we become aware of a thought pattern developing in our minds, we avoid inhibiting it or changing it; instead we just allow it to unfold and flow on, watching the stages it goes through, but not identifying with it, or actively participating in it.

If we do this, we gradually find ourselves becoming focussed in the part of our minds which is unrestricted by limits, which is free to roam anywhere, anywhen. This part of our mind is the key to our relationship with the Soul.

We will not be able to carry right through this exercise of

meditation at once. We will have to keep making attempts, seeking to train hidden muscles and groups of cells in our brains to ease into activity to which they are unaccustomed, and then to become more and more adept. But if we give a short time each day to this practice – even only fifteen minutes – we will see improvement and this improvement will increase the faster as we continue.

When we get to the stage where we can quite easily retire into that inner part of our minds, and observe the through traffic of the outer part without getting drawn into it, we can begin more purposefully to identify with the Soul.

We draw our attention in from even watching the flow of our mind activity as it comes and goes. We hold our attention poised and contained now, at the very heart of our awareness, or conscious mind. This is a point of great power and creative potential, and should be carried out with full recognition of its significance. We are gathering into a concentrated focus all our personality force, and we are holding it in the control of our own will, so that we can then make with it an act of directed, intentional purpose.

That moment comes and we look upwards to the Soul with the eye of the mind which we have held concentrated at the centre of our essential being. We inwardly look upwards towards the Soul, and we simultaneously listen for the vibration of the Soul. The full and concentrated attention of the essence of ourself is turned upon the Soul; we have only to wait, maintaining as we do, this focussed looking and listening. The response of the Soul may not be immediately apparent. We may have to keep practising this exercise many times before we sense any tangible manifestation of the presence and active participation of the Soul.

But it will come and it will influence our sense of self and of poise in small ways at first, then steadily in more and more extended ways.

It is important to practise this approach to the Soul regularly, at least once each day; and yet not more than about fifteen minutes should be given at each sitting.

This is for two reasons:

a. You are using sensitive neurones in the brain that are not accustomed to having such an intense, concentrated demand made upon them; they can be overstrained, and, just as muscles in back, legs, or arms, should be very gently trained to smoothly and easily carry out this new work.

b. Focussing yourself inwards in this way results in a stimulation of the pituitary gland; also, as soon as you expose
   yourself to contact with the Soul, this contact will come – even
   if you yourself are not at first aware of it – and it is intensely
   stimulating. This stimulation can be difficult to handle. Both
   the pineal and the pituitary glands are activated into greater
   vitality and you may find your mind open to an enormous
   new field of idea activity. This is very exciting and fills your
   life with new scope and inspiration, but it can also leave you
   unstabilised and with a very over-stimulated nervous system.
   It is essential to go gently and cautiously at this work so that
   you have time to adjust to the inflow that will follow your
   approach to the Soul, to process it and to integrate it into your
   current perception of reality and life.

There is one further point worth remembering. Contact with the
Soul is largely about light. When we turn on our relationship
with the Soul, we turn on an intense light into our life. This light
will immediately illuminate the darkness and shadows in our
life. The early stages of contact with the Soul usually bring not
only positive stimulation, inspiration and fresh, renewed energy,
but also a horrified awareness of our weakness, our limitation,
our arrogance and our hypocrisy. We clear away these cobwebs
by allowing the light and love of the Soul to melt them and
dissolve them into nothingness; so we deal with the process by
exposing ourself further to the very light which is illuminating
our own darkness. But we emphasise now, our identification
with the love element of the Soul and this helps us to love
ourselves, as all humanity, in spite of, or as well as, our
weaknesses.

The capacity to identify with the Love aspect of the Soul does
not come immediately for most of us. When we first make our
approach to the Soul, we are actively using only our mental
aspect. We have relaxed the body and stilled our feelings, so that
our minds can be free of interference and distraction from these
levels. Our mind, our inner eye and inner ear ever so alertly
tuned, makes its approach to the Soul. It is at first only sensitive
enough to be able to respond to the rhythm of the Knowledge
petals of the Soul. So what we first make contact with is the
outermost activity or aspect of the Soul, its most dense and
tangible rhythmic vibration. It is this outer ring of Knowledge

petals which vibrate with light. Light emanates from this Soul aspect and it is this light which our minds, in meditation, become steadily more aware of and more stimulated and inspired by.

But it is the Light of Knowledge inspiring our mental faculties. It is very important to understand this in order to be able to recognise what is happening to us as we carry through the process of unfolding our relationship with the Soul. The mind is an organ of analysis, of perception and of detachment. It has the capacity to see Love and to analyse it, to direct and to order, but not to feel it.

So the effect of our mental attunement to the rhythm of the outermost layer of the Soul body will be experienced as a sharpening of our thought processes. Our minds will find it easier to stand back from our emotional turbulence, to perceive from a greater perspective the elements at work around and within us; we will find it easier to organise our thoughts, to be clear and to see right into the depths of a matter. And we will experience new vitality in our ideas and therefore in our projections into the future.

In time, it will become automatic for our minds to vibrate in rhythm with the Knowledge petals of the Soul; we will find ourselves aligning inwardly with the Soul even when in the midst of outer crises in our lives. This capacity will enable us to release into our life circumstances a new source of energy and understanding; it will give us fresh scope and power to harmonise events around us.

Our first step of approach to the Soul has been accomplished. There can be no turning back, but it is time for the second step of approach to be made.

This involves our emotional nature beginning to become consciously attuned to the second ring of petals of the Soul body – the Love petals. This can only begin to take place when our minds flow with ease into rhythm with the Knowledge petals. When this relationship begins there is usually some conflict. The Light of the Soul illuminates the dark shadows hiding away in corners of our psyche; emotionally we tense and withdraw from seeing our own negativity, from taking responsibility for the sides of ourself that we would prefer to ignore. So along with the stimulation of our new contact with the Soul there also inevitably come frustration, emotional tension and resistance and also fear:

fear of taking responsibility for ironing out all the humps and bumps and creases in our nature.

Emotionally we will be enlivened and refreshed and invigorated by the stimulation our minds are receiving, but we will also experience a new, more subtle depth of self-confrontation.

The step that brings new healing and balance to this is a renewal of our approach to the Soul. But this fresh approach comes not only from our minds, but also from our hearts: the uncertainty and self-doubt in our hearts cries out for guidance and reassurance from the Soul. As we sit in meditation, preparing ourself carefully through physical and emotional quiescence, to gather and concentrate our force at the point within the essence of our minds that we now are quite familiar with, we also gather to that same point the strength of our emotional confusion; instead of allowing ourselves to be drawn down into the stormy seas of that confusion, we, through our purpose and intention, gather the strength of that emotional turbulence and lift it up to become one with our focussed, mental attentiveness. Before, we had the power of our mental alertness gathered and contained, ready to take that leap of attention towards the Soul; now we add to our gathered mental alertness, the emotional strength of the moment (and if we have recently been in emotional turmoil, this will be great); we gather this in and hold it contained along with our mental alertness; . . . and then we direct both our controlled mental attentiveness, and our concentrated emotional force, towards the Soul.

In making the effort to gather into our control, our emotional strength, we have awakened our inner emotional nature to greater activity of a positive kind, and stimulated thereby, the Heart centre. The inner emanation of this centre is very, very sensitive and refined and when it is carried up towards the Soul along with the inner rhythm of the mental body, the rhythm of the Love petals of the Soul begins to be felt and responded to by the personality.

For most of us it will not be easy to identify the activity of our Heart centres, the inner, very very delicate rhythm of our emotional natures. It is easy to connect with the outer, more crude aspect of our emotions: we know when we experience fear, or insecurity, anger or jealousy; but what lies beneath these feelings? If we step back from our personal fear, and the circumstances that surround this, what do we find? If we do the same with our other emotions, including our wanting and our desire, what lies beneath these too? It is the feelings that lie at the heart of our outer, very personal emotions, that opens the door to the innermost, exquisitely sensitive, essence of our emotional nature. And it is only through becoming aware of these that we can attune ourselves to the rhythm of the Love petals of the Soul, the middle ring of petals.

Only by attuning ourselves to this inner rhythm can we learn to draw back from any personal emotional confusion and gather the force of our emotional strength into a focussed, controlled point which we are then able to use as a means to a source of new energy: the very thing which seems to destroy us (our emotional tumult which shatters and uncordinates us), when we learn to draw ourselves in to its essential source, we then become master of, so that we control and direct its course and pathway. We harness the demon of our own unruly emotions and get it to work for us, according to our wishes and intention.

We can only do this once we are able to listen to and identify with the inner essence of our emotional nature.

There is really one feeling which lies at the heart of our emotional nature, and this is a yearning for oneness. It is our sense of separation and isolation which causes us to get caught up in fear and anger, jealousy and insecurity. Being human involves experience as an individual identity and yet at the root of ourselves is an insatiable ache for at-one-ment: we are fragments of the one spirit imprisoned in bundles of physical cell tissue that limit and contain that spirit, whilst nevertheless enabling it to mould and shape, explore and experiment, with the element of physical matter, in space. Yet at root that spirit yearns to demonstrate the underlying oneness of all life: that within our shapes and forms and personality, so diverse and varied in expression and life-aim, there lives and moves and has its Being, the One spirit, the One Life Essence.

When we bring to our second step of approach to the Soul, the strength of our emotional yearning, but condensed into its essential nature, the ache for at-one-ment, the rhythm of our inner mental nature, and of our inner emotional nature, are harmonised and together they amount to a more intense opening of approach to the Soul, than the mental aspect alone can make. This intensity, subtle though it is, penetrates to the Love petals and draws from them a fresh radiation towards the personality.

As we practise this new step, day after day, the vibratory rhythm of our Heart centres becomes more and more in tune with that of the Love petals. This in turn brings a further unfoldment in the at-one-ment of the rhythms of the mind and the Knowledge petals. There is steadily more harmony, less dissonance, between these; their attunement becomes without tension, effortless: they are one. This has a further effect upon the rhythmic harmony of the emotional nature and Love petals; it becomes surer, more relaxed.

Our thought-life relaxes as the at-one-ment of rhythms flows more easily; it becomes imbued with the vibration of love. It continues to become clearer, more acute and dynamic in its capacity to analyse and to understand, yet all these elements are now enriched and made fuller by the presence of Love: Light gains depth and tone through Love. We more easily find ourselves able to stand back from our personal emotional difficulties, to see the humorous side of events, and to fit our emotional tensions into a larger context whereupon they become part of our shared state of humanness, no longer something to bring us down and to destroy us, but instead a part of the wondrous tapestry of life, so rich and varied. We begin to learn how to turn our emotional turbulence into a creative power for good or for enrichment; we learn to ride our emotional force like birds ride currents of air, or small boats the ocean; we learn to flow with them and to dance with them, in constant worship of the wonder that is life, when good and bad can be brought into harmony within us.

The capacity to attune to the rhythm of the Love petals of the Soul will bring a very profound change into our experience of ourselves. It will have a softening and a mellowing effect upon us; our nervous systems will begin to get some respite from the intense stimulation of our contact with the Knowledge petals.

This mellowing and softening prepares us for our third step of approach. This stage involves the etheric body (the inner aspect of our physical body) attuning itself to the rhythm of the Sacrifice petals, the innermost ring of the Soul body.

Before we can identify and communicate through our etheric body, we have to have reached a very deep understanding and attunement with our physical body, and all aspects of our life affected by it: it is not possible to master or direct the inner aspect of either mental, emotional or physical bodies until we have developed a refined awareness and control of their outer counterparts.

Where the physical body is concerned this implies an ability to order creatively all aspects of our life that concern our physical survival. So we are thinking not only of our physical health and harmony, and our capacity to express our thoughts and feelings through our physical bodies, but also of our career or work, our home and its maintenance, and our transport – that which enables our bodies to be mobile and so to carry through any intention concerning our physical survival. These three things – career, home and transport – enable us to maintain our worldly life upon Earth; order and harmony in this area of our life make it possible for us to express and demonstrate, to make manifest and real, all that our minds are inspired with through our unfolding relationship with the Soul.

When the relationship with the Soul has unfolded so far that our minds and hearts pulse in rhythm as one, and are able at will to attune themselves also to a oneness and harmony with the rhythmic pulse of the Knowledge and Love petals, it will become possible for us tentatively to reach out towards the Sacrifice petals, the innermost ring with the most delicate and sensitive, yet potent and transformative, rhythm of vibration.

The magnetic rapport between the Soul and the personality is by now so real and vibrant that this last stage of at-one-ment may creep up on us without any deliberate effort on our part. Or, the intensifying illumination of our thoughts, and ripening fullness of our sense of devotion to human need, may stimulate a further reaching out from us into our surrender to the vibration of the Soul. Surrender is a key word concerning the petals of Sacrifice, and also the Base centre, the centre which is most affected by this approach deeper into the heart of the Soul.

The personality has, bit by bit, surrendered the dominance of its own rhythm, and invited the Soul to embrance and envelope this with its rhythm. The impulse came at first from a desperate cry for help from the personality; but the impulse continues more and more from the desire to carry through the inner transformation experienced by the personality through the influence of the Soul vibration. This transformation draws one closer and closer into awareness of the oneness of all life, and the will to direct one's creative energy towards living out this oneness and enabling it to be more apparent than it is, in the world around us.

We surrender ourself more and more to the oneness; we let go of our tight holding on to our differentness, our isolation, and our separateness.

The Base centre will usually be found to be very, very tight –

we grip, in fists of fear, our will to survive, and to be ourselves. As we become more at-oned with the rhythm of the Soul, this centre is softened and loosened by its transformative radiations. We almost imperceptibly find ourselves directing our efforts more towards group needs and group survival and identity; we find ourselves less anxious about our own identity and its maintenance. And we experience the joy of reward and fulfilment from our participation in group needs. We grow very aware of what we need as individuals to survive and we learn easily to fulfill these needs – but these are basic and minimal, not excessive or self-centred. We discover that by tending to these, we release more energy and creative potential for our involvement in the group.

Gradually we re-order our lives so that we are housed, clothed and fed according to our personal characteristic needs, and we learn to keep our bodies flexible and agile, vital and alert. The more we achieve harmony in these things, the more we are able to bring inspiration and fresh energy into the lives of others, and this activity in turn nourishes and fulfils our sense of belonging and of having a useful, valuable part to play in the community of life's journey.

This is the result of surrendering at an ever deeper level, the vibration of the personal will and identity to the influence of the Soul. The first approach, through the mind, to the Knowledge petals, leads one deeper into an ability to sense, to hear and to feel and to see, the rhythm emanating from the Soul. Seeing, hearing and feeling carries us eventually into oneness with that which we see, hear and feel; we become that which we sense, and we become transformed into a more sensitive, subtle and finely-tuned instrument as a result. We are carried deeper into ever more delicate yet wondrous rhythms: into and through the Love petals till we become absorbed also into the rhythm of the Sacrifice petals.

When we have achieved absorption into the rhythm of the Sacrifice petals we will also find that the aspects of our personality, our mental, emotional and physical bodies, are more harmonised and integrated than they were. We will find ourself able to function as a well-tuned instrument at last. The chord produced by these three sounding together will be harmonious and resonant and clear. Soul and personality will be one; they will produce one sound, one vibration, one radiation. It then becomes possible for us to approach the Spiritual Triad in a conscious way.

Our relationship with the spiritual Triad follows the same path of unfoldment as our relationship with the Soul: first the mental body and the Knowledge petals as one tune in to the rhythm of Manas, the most accessible aspect of the Spiritual Triad, which is pure mind; next these, at-oned with the emotional body and the Love petals, tune themselves to Buddhi, which is the essence of love; and finally, these, at-oned with the physical-etheric and the Sacrifice petals, tune themselves to Atma, which is the source of will or purpose, the intention to exist and to be.

During the absorption into the rhythmic vibration of the Soul we make contact with our Master, and also with our group at a spiritual level. Further exploration deeper into the transformative relationship with the Spiritual Triad will be monitored and governed by the Master and does not require attention here. As soon as we begin to identify with the Love petals of the Soul, our understanding of the process we are unfolding gains depth and clarity, and we need less and less guidance from outside ourselves.

We learn how to be taught, and to have our questions answered, by turning inwards and attuning ourselves to the rhythm of the Soul. Carried to us in that rhythm are the words we need to hear, the visions we need to see, and the feelings we need to clothe ourselves with. Our deeper penetration to the petals of Sacrifice is accompanied always by this inner, constant revelation of meaning and purpose.

THE EFFECTS OF UNFOLDING SOUL CONTROL

Our relationship with the Soul leads us into a more and more sensitive awareness of group activity. We begin to see that all of life is fundamentally about relationship, and that the elements participating in any relationship form 'a group'. Any group in this sense is a dynamic and constantly changing entity. A pattern will be recognisable in its form, and it may unfold and grow, as energy flows and expresses itself through it,acording to a discernible pattern. The sensitive eye will recognise this pattern and be able to respond to it.

The group in this sense will take form and dissolve again, its various elements flowing into relationship with other elements with which it forms new groups and patterns of flow, according to need or exploratory whim. This is how cells work within our bodies; it is how we function in the community of the human race; and it is how we function, as soul-infused personalities, in the realm of Souls and Soul-groups. At each level there is a personal identity, form or pattern of force: each cell has a degree of individuality, in both shape and function; each individual personality also has an identity all its own; at the Soul level too are to be found differentiations. At the level of the Soul these are expressed in terms of intensity of essence, whilst at the cellular level they emphasise outward form and appearance.

We made our first approach to the Soul through our minds, the mental aspect of our personality. This approach stimulates the Soul to respond by becoming more active in its transmission of energy towards us. The transmission is received by the Heart centre, which is stimulated by it to a stronger, more expansive pulse and activity. The result is that the Heart centre unfolds more rapidly than it otherwise could. Unfoldment of the Heart centre always means a stronger awareness in us of the needs of others, and a growing urge, in whatever way we can, to serve those needs. If we are a healer, we offer ourselves as agents for the dissolving away of the distress of others, so that they may draw closer to awareness of their own spiritual identity, and their capacity to live their lives from a point of connectedness to this.

We will be confronted with all sorts of problems and conflict in this effort, and through tackling these, and allowing ourselves always to be guided by listening to the Soul, we will grow in depth of understanding, and awareness of life processes. These unfolding qualities will result in us becoming steadily more decentralised. The focus of our inner burning will move away from the self and its desires and needs; we will lose ourselves in our effort to serve the needs of others, and find in doing so that many of our own problems and needs will be dealt with, or will simply melt away . . . we will find that, almost without realising what was happening, we have become group-oreintated. Our thoughts and actions will quite naturally spring from our group-identification rather than from our personal wishes.

Our involvement with our spiritual group, via the Soul, will at this stage be extensive, whether or not we are conscious of this.

The Soul is at one in vibratory rhythm with the spiritual group; as we open ourselves to receive and be absorbed into the rhythm of the Soul, so our identification with this group expands. It gives us strength and stability, nourishment and soothing.

Our dedication to the unfoldment of our relationship with the Soul to some extent draws us away from our previous contacts and way of relating to the world; we can feel vulnerable, isolated and lonely; the relationship is like a delicate and unusual plant: but to flourish and grow strong it needs to be tended with care, and sometimes granted special conditions and protection, like a hothouse plant. Others may draw back from contact with us at this time; we may seem in-turned and self-preoccupied in a way they cannot understand. When our relationship with the Soul is firm and strong and we are sure and confident in it, we can re-expose ourselves once more to all social conditions and connections without it being damaged. In the meantime, our awareness that our relationship with the Soul opens us also to our spiritual group sustains us and replaces what we seem unable to find out in the world.

Our capacity to merge in oneness with our spiritual group, and, indeed, with the Soul itself, can be strengthened and eased if we work in the visible world with a group in meditation which is designed to unfold the relationship with the Soul. To work in this way in group form can balance and harmonise the chances of becoming over-stimulated by our approach to the Soul. A stronger inflow from the Soul will usually be invoked by a group than by an individual, yet this inflow will be distributed in a harmonic way throughout the group. Individual needs will be adjusted more quickly and smoothly when we work together in group form, and the discussion which takes place afterwards, in the Light of Knowledge with which the Soul has illumined the group mind, will be deeply nourishing: the sharing of understanding found, as of difficulties unresolved, will have a wonderfully enriching effect upon each member of the group.

However, it is important to choose the people with whom we intend to work like this very carefully, and also to make sure, before we start, that our aims are to develop our relationship with the Soul, and not to air personality grievances, or to find new scope for our little egos. If we need to do these things, we can do them in other groups. A group in which personal egos are active will fail to make any meaningful connection with the Soul; the Light of Knowledge and the Love of Wisdom will not be able to be absorbed by the vibrations of minds caught in the corridors of the personal ego, and so nothing of a transformative nature will take place.

We are all involved with our personal egos to some extent, but when we make a sincere approach to the Soul, and expose the rhythm of our own inner minds to the emanation of the Soul, these become overshadowed and mellowed by it: our inner being grows ripe and we begin to experience the fruit of the tree of human unfoldment.

Through our efforts to unfold our relationship with the Soul we move inwards towards the community of spiritual beingness, a community characterised more by intensity of essence, than by visible shape and form. Yet we simultaneously move outwards, through the expansion of the Heart centre which our Soul contact stimulates, towards the community of humanness and human neediness, a community most readily accessible through its visible state and condition.

This two way outward and inward movement provides us with an orientation which is much expanded; reaching out to that new orientation will temporarily cause in us confusion and uncertainty of identity; but gradually, the light of the Soul will show the way, and we will place ourselves anew in a deeper and broader landscape. Our thought and actions take on the dimensions of this expanded landscape: we can see both inwardly and outwardly for miles and miles and miles: and the previous orientation of being imprisoned in a seething cage of confusion is transformed into a sense of being granted the key to a boundless garden filled with new things to explore. Perhaps we will lose our way and be unable to retrace our steps back to ourself? But the gate into the garden only appears to us when we are in full awareness of our connection inwards (and upwards) with the Soul, and outwards (and downwards), with Mother Earth; the silver thread of this awareness is our orientation: we have only to think this alive within us to immediately know who and where we are. We become explorers in spiritual space!

The three stages of absorption of the personality into the Soul are accompanied by an increasing awareness in us of our participation in group activity on different levels. It is also accompanied by subtle changes in the distribution of our personal energy. These changes influence the state of vitality of the centres in our bodies, and, through this, and in time, the cell structure and activity itself.

The first approach to the Soul, via the mental faculty, will bring a particular emphasis of stimulation to the Head centres, and, to some extent, to the Throat centre. The Head centres are the Crown (pineal gland) and the Third Eye (pituitary), and the cells directly responsive to the glands of these centres will experience a flushing out of tension, stiffness, toxins and inactivity, at the same time receiving a stimulation to better tone, flexibility, clear cell development and dynamic activity.

The second approach to the Soul will have a similar effect of purification, rearrangement and stimulation, upon the cells responsive, through the Heart centre, to the heart, lungs and thymus, and also the digestive organs, through the Solar Plexus centre. Both Pelvic and Throat centres will also be influenced by this stage.

Thirdly, the Base and Crown centres will receive an intense purification and stimulation, which will have a very integrating, rounding-out effect upon the whole unfoldment of the personality, leaving it infinitely better able to function in the fullness of creativity, as an agent of spiritual intention in the arena of the world.

As healers, each phase of intense purification and stimulation of the centres will leave us aware of being able to achieve a deeper, more direct and one-pointed effect upon our patient's energy problems. We will feel more aware of the energy flowing through us to our patient, of its volume and of its intensity, of the pulse of its rhythm, and of how much or how little we can control it, and also of when it is appropriate to exert control and when it is appropriate to stand back and withhold all effort.

The results of our healing work will be more quickly apparent and we will grow more sensitively aware of the stages the healing is following, and of how to be more accurate and precise in our interpretation of these.

With greater ability, there always also comes greater responsibility . . . we find ourselves given work of more profound implications than at first; this will challenge us, but, as always, it is our Soul control which governs us: if we sincerely offer ourselves to the Soul, and withhold all ambition or ego-centred intention from our work, the Soul will work through us, and be enabled to carry through the work it seeks to do. It can be both strengthening and soothing to call upon the spiritual group as well as the Soul, when we feel asked to take on particularly responsible work.

The more we are willing to accept the responsibility offered us, the more infused will our personalities become with the presence of the Soul; this again is a factor in intensifying the unfolding relationship, and in bringing about further stages of purification and stimulation of our own centres and cell tissue.

We will find that our bodies demand new sustaining patterns in order to carry, free of problems, the higher frequency of vibration that we become more consistently exposed to. We will have to pay new attention to the quality and amount of oxygen, purity of water, and regularity of exercise that we tend our bodies with. And we will also find ourselves having to re-assess our ability to make use of different types of foods, in order to discover which ones our organs can make the most efficient use of. This is a very personal matter, as there are many different types, each with its own needs. Requiring the Soul to teach us how to take best care of ourselves is an important part of our learning how to use our intuitive faculty. We have to learn how to heal ourselves, through tuning in to the energy state of each moment, and assessing its requirements on many different levels, if we are to be able to really heal others.

CONCLUSION

Our relationship with the Soul is the key to self-transformation at all levels of existence. We seek that key when our experience of life imprisons and negates us. It is the key which opens for us the door into the most safe, yet magical and wondrous, journey of discovery. Marking the way, like milestones along the road, are our three approaches to the Soul, each one tuning us up so we can hear a faster, lighter, higher vibration, each one transforming us, even at a cellular level, so we can receive, carry and transmit, a higher frequency of energy. And, all the while, our sense grows, of being absorbed into the community of Souls, whilst simultaneously feeling more purposeful in the community of human beings. We seem to be transformed into a being that extends in all directions further, yet is simultaneously more focussed at its centre. Life more abundantly flows and flows through us; life more intensely burns and burns and ever burns. . .

ANALYSIS OF THE RADIATION OF LOVE
MEDITATION FORM

The whole form is about learning to flow consciously and readily between the invisible and visible aspects of life so that the invisible essence may be made more apparent for others.

Although the meditation is an act of devotion in communication, this analysis is expressed in the scientific language of light and energy, i.e. differing rates of frequency of vibration of light. We move from awareness of slow frequency, (our dense, concrete, material reality) to awareness of high frequency, (or subtle, ethereal, 'spiritual' reality): from the outer to the inner, and back again.

1. Focus upon the physical, most material, dense, tangible, outer, slow frequency via the initial group link or concentration inward. Move gradually through feeling, emotional and thinking or mental bodies – ever-increasing frequencies, and the mechanism whereby the rapid frequency light of the 'spiritual' plane expresses itself in the outer, visible plane of the tangible world.

2. Having steadied and relaxed the three aspects of this outer mechanism we make conscious our already existing link with the spiritual plane through identification with the Soul, or point of concentrated spiritual force. This pure and impersonal force is used to cleanse further the earthly mechanism – this cleansing bathes and infuses the low frequency mechanism with high frequency light – the inspiration and the magical transformative work of the meditation is begun.

3. Fusion of personal consciousness focussed in the Soul with the spiritual identity of the whole group – mergence of diversity into invisible, yet potent and high frequency union and harmony.

4. Invocation of Divine Love.

5. As a new, group identity of focussed intention, radiation of Divine Love in ever-widening ripples.

6. Return of focussed group intention to the group and concentration of the Divine Flow upon a specific and personalised area of distress.

These last two steps are the high point of the meditation; they are the conscious use and directed radiation of the invisible, high

MEDITATION ON THE RADIATION OF LOVE

We observe the activity of our mind . . . without interfering with its pace or rhythm we simply watch it for a moment or two . . . we let ourself sink away from any sense of tightness or holding in our mind, so that it is left free to float and drift.

Now we watch the air as it fills up our lungs like a balloon, and then empties again . . . we don't seek to control this flow, just observe the wave of air as it flows down into the chest and then once more up and out. And now we feel that this wave of air is rippling right over our whole body from the top of the head, over chest, abdomen, legs and feet to the ground, and then up the whole length of our body once more to the top of the head . . . we let ourselves harmonise with the rhythm that we are observing. Feel roots and tendrils reaching from the body right down into the heart of the Earth, holding us stabilised and safe . . . now we feel that our body is very, very soft . . . and that it is very, very light . . . that if someone touched us their hand would sink into nothingness.

The love and light of the Soul draws our thoughts gently into its arena of influence; the love emanating from the Soul heals, soothes and nourishes us; the presence of the Soul fills our entire being with a cross of love and light which purifies and protects us. Our hearts beat as one; our thoughts think as one.

Divine Love, so fill us with Yourself, that we may become all Love, and let us in the power of your Love, within us, suffuse all beings with thoughts of love, compassion, joy and peace.

As a group we are a great lung, drawing in, as one, the life of the Soul, and pouring this out gradually further and further like ripples on a lake, through our immediate environment, through our whole country, through oppressed people throughout the world, through the whole of humanity, through the animal kingdom, the vegetable kingdom, and the mineral kingdom, to heal and nourish and revitalise.

We draw our thoughts back to our immediate group, and bring people we know to be in distress, into the emanatory influence of the group.

We gently let go the magnetic pull of the group Soul . . . we recognise our contact with our personal Soul, and once more feel the protective cross of love filling our whole being . . . we become aware of ourselves as individuals and we feel again roots and tendrils reaching from our bodies, right down into the heart of the Earth, anchoring and grounding us. We feel the firm solidity of our body, the warm comfort and physicalness of the earth beneath us.

We say the great invocation and sound the OM . . .

Meditation

frequency light contacted, into the tangible and low frequency world.

7. Gentle, step-by-step return into the low frequency world and into individual and tangible consciousness; separation of the individual from the group consciousness in order to continue individual life in form in the dimension of the physical world.

8. The final sharing is then an attempt to anchor and concretise for consistent further learning the experience and learning of the inner, invisible journey into the spiritual dimension.

The whole form is about learning consciously and readily to flow between the invisible and visible aspects of life so that the invisible essence may be made more apparent for others.

A SHORT DAILY MEDITATION ROUTINE

As we tune up our personality vehicles to receive and transmit ever more dynamic and vital force, or light, we find that this light highlights the beauty and wonder in life, but also the shadows and darkness. These stand out in ever sharper contrast, particularly those that we become aware of in ourselves. This tends to draw our attention to ourselves, and because that attention is more and more dynamic, as we gain access more and more to 'spiritual' and dynamic light, we can actually make our problem worse, and find it more and more difficult to let go of. We find ourselves preoccupied with aspects of ourselves, yet at the same time chastising ourselves for paying so much attention to ourselves. The aim behind the following very simple meditation routine is to strike a balance in this problem by allotting a certain amount of time each day for focussing completely upon the self, and also for learning how to regulate its unfoldment in a more ordered and less haphazard way. By giving the personal self one's total attention for a short while its needs begin to be met, and it can then be freed for dealing with the needs of the day in a more wholehearted fashion.

Please also bear in mind the thought that life (God) is energy, and energy is light; so God is light, and also whole (hole) and one; but energy is in constant motion, as light is also. Light moves in a spectrum of rates of vibration, from very fast to very slow. What we call Spirit, and the spiritual plane, is simply light at a fast rate of vibration, whilst what we call Matter, and the physical, earthly plane, is light moving at a slow rate of vibration. Some people are evolutionarily receptive to light moving at a fast rate, whilst others are not (through all the varying rates of the spectrum). The task of the healer is to make available fast-moving light to those who cannot as yet handle this alone. So you are aiming to perfect and make conscious your natural ability to receive and transmit fast-moving light.

MORNING: Make contact with the Soul; it is a focal point for energy qualified by love and light. See your mundane self, the three-fold personality, soften; see it becoming receptive to the Soul. Your three-fold being is in an attitude of receptivity upwards towards the positive attitude of the Soul. See the column of love leading from the Soul and very carefully ground it in the Earth beneath you; do not seek to focus the love or light of the Soul in yourself: this leads to overstimulation. The attention of your mind is drawn gently up towards the Soul; enquire of this point of deepened perception, what quality you should seek to bring to the day which lies ahead of you. Allow the response to be explored by the mind and seek to fix the core thought in your consciousness. Say the Great Invocation.

It may be necessary at times, when you feel preoccupied with tiredness, or mental worries, to scan the condition of your etheric, emotional and mental vehicles, and then to adjust them by seeing them one by one becoming calm and stable, and by letting go of their tension or hyperactivity. This should be done after earthing your column of love, but before seeking direction for your day.

NOON: If possible take five minutes to align with the Soul, to scan your three-fold vehicles, and to reaffirm yourself as a channel linking the spiritual realm with the material realm for the free circulation of love.

End with the Great Invocation or the mantra: We know, O lord of Light and Love, about the need, touch our hearts anew with love that we may love and give.

BEFORE BED: Five minutes once more for realignment, quick scan of the state of each vehicle, and then a scan of the day as an attempt to assess to what extent one has managed to bring the quality perceived in the morning meditation, to the handling of the day.

Divine Light
proceeding from the splendour
of the ineffable Godhead,
I worship and adore Thee!
Lead me from the unreal to the real;
lead me from darkness to light;
lead me from death to immortality.

Serene Light
shining in the ground of my being,
Draw me to Yourself!
Draw me past the snares of the senses,
out of the mazes of the mind.
Free me from symbols, from words,
That I may discover
The Signified,
The Word Unspoken
In the darkness which veils the ground of my being.

Figure 24

ORIGINS

The information offered you here in this book comes essentially from within myself. Many people at this time are hungrily gathering information on the subject of healing from all the traditional sources, then evolving through this, their own partic- ular and individual approach. It is right that we should take what our ancient human culture offers us, and add to and evolve this further in the light of our own experience, and in response to modern needs. Our skills deepen and enrichen as a result, and we in turn have a broader understanding to offer those that follow after us.

My own journey into healing began in 1979, after a near-death experience. Under the anaesthetic I had a brief but intense experience which changed my whole life. In the months that followed I sought to make positive all that had been negative in my life. Two branches unfolded: I began to study and practise reflexology and shiatsu, and I sought a religious discipline I could accept, in order to develop and express my spiritual identity.

The manual work of reflexology and shiatsu quickly brought me a local reputation as one who really could help with a variety of problems, both emotional and physical. I acquired all the books I could find on these subjects, and hungrily absorbed them in order to extend my skills. I was at the same time reading books on physiology and metabolism, and looking at pictures on the structure of the body.

My hunt for a spiritual discipline led me eventually to the Arcane School and the wonderful extended material supplied by the Alice Bailey writings. I became a student of the Arcane School in 1981 and am still following their course of work, involving progressive meditation work, study and written work.

This course is designed for people who wish to pursue 'discipleship in the New Age'. For me I found bit by bit that I was able more consciously to use my brain as a tool through which I could bring myself into attunement with my own spiritual identity, the Soul, and in time with my own Master and his Ashram, or group of workers in the spiritual dimension. The word 'attunement' is very apt, as the process is exactly like tuning a musical instrument, only it is our own brain that we learn to tune. This is not a skill reserved for the few, or the gifted; it is the heritage of all who possess a brain, but it does require dedication, and the heart, as well as the mind, must be fully open to the process, if it is to succeed.

At this stage I was rising at 5.30 am in order to meditate and study before my daily duties, as a farmer's wife and mother of young children, pressed in upon my time and energy.

Bit by bit my manual work with people merged with the unfolding spiritual relationship with the Soul, until one day I felt that my hands were being pushed away from my patient's body and to my surprise my fingertips registered the flow of energy through the points I was using, with even greater sensitivity than when they had been touching the physical body.

This was a dramatic turning point for me as I was now working with the 'etheric vehicle': the 'body', form or shape in the etheric field from which the physical body 'condenses', or becomes solid.

I found my work was more potent, and that my attunement with the Soul, before, during and after working with someone, was essential and intense. I was very strict in my use of 'spiritual hygiene' i.e. the heartfelt use of the mantras to begin and end a session, the careful alignment with the Soul before a session, and whenever necessary during one, and the dipping of the hands in water immediately a session was over, in order to neutralise static electricity.

I also found that my sense of my patient's energy state became much more acute. Bit by bit my understanding of the inter-relatedness of the Centres grew, and this connected with beautiful integrity with the particular area of effect governed by each meridian point. It seemed that in the stillness and deep concentration of a session, the Soul was able to cast onto the quiescent, aligned and receptive surface of the mind, images concerning the connections within the body, and the patterns formed by these connections. I was (and still am) constantly in delight at the beauty, and fundamental simplicity, of the patterns created by the connectedness of energy flowing within and without us; and also shocked at how stuck and blocked these connections become, yet how readily they will respond to unblocking when given appropriate conditions.

So much information seemed to be being made available to me at this time, simply through the act of me putting myself in the position of aligning with the Soul on behalf of the needs of my patient. I was not able to put much of it on paper although I did begin to do this as people began to come to me in order to learn. What I did spend a lot of time doing was cross-referencing the information I was becoming aware of. I was very cautious initially of absolutely accepting this information without checking, if I could, that it fitted in with the knowledge and experience of others. The books listed in the bibliography that follows are some of those that I would have used for this purpose.

Eventually my most important source of self-affirmation came from my patients. I have very few dissatisfied patients. It became clear that the Key of the Centres was an extremely accurate tool for understanding a patient's individual problem. To adjust the health through the application of this key bit by bit enables a better integration of the patient's physical, emotional, mental and even spiritual aspects. Life can be lived more fully and more richly as a result, and the ability to deal creatively with ongoing problems can unfold, so that he or she no longer need feel a victim of circumstance or bad luck.

At this time I am a full-time healer, although I am moving rapidly into developing my skills a stage further. The writing of this book was a work of devotion and dedication. It seemed to flow out of the depths of me. I had initially to put myself into a condition of deep concentration, but then the words and images seemed to tumble forth as if they had been waiting too long to be released onto the page, and their own journey of sharing and nourishment for others. Completing the book has freed me to work further on new ideas that are pressing themselves out from within me: I am currently exploring ideas for working at energy-adjustment through movement in order to be able to work with groups more effectively.

In a way the book I have written is the kind of book I would have liked to have had in the early stages of my learning. It is my sincere wish that it will provide a bridge for many into a deepened ability to help others who are suffering at this time. If this comes about then my effort will not have been in vain!

The following is a list of some of the books that I have found useful over the years:

The many books of Alice Bailey, published by the Lucis Trust, Suite 54, 3 Whitehall Court, SW1A 2EF, are rich in material related to the deeper purpose and significance of life upon Earth. Alice Bailey spent about 20 years (from the twenties to the forties of this century) as the amanuensis for the Tibetan Master Djwhal Khul. The information made available in these books gives us a wealth of study material on the nature of God, the present state of humanity and our possible future direction, healing, the Soul, Jesus and the Christ, meditation, discipleship. They are written with tremendous lovingness and understanding. They are also written in an authoritative way, even though it is advised that their content should be tested whenever possible in our life experience. The 'scientific' attitude is recommended in this sense: that the material should be regarded with an open mind, as possible and reasonable until proved otherwise, and that until it is proved otherwise we should put it to the test in our day-to-day observation and experience of life.

A Treatise on Esoteric Healing
A Treatise on White Magic
A Treatise on Esoteric Psychology Vols 1 and 2
From Intellect to Intuition
Letters on Occult Meditation
Problems of Humanity
Glamour: A World Problem
The Consciousness of the Atom
Telepathy

All the above by Alice Bailey.

Other books which discuss the subtler, less obvious aspects of our human relationship with the invisible worlds:

The Death and Resurrection Show: Rogan Taylor (Anthony Blond, 1985)

Sensitive Chaos: Theodor Schwenk (Rudolf Steiner Press, 1965)

Passages: A Guide for Pilgrims of the Mind: Andersen and Savary (Turnstone, 1972)

The Grand Design: Patrick Francis (Regency Press, 1987)

A New Science of Life: Rupert Sheldrake (Blond and Briggs)

Books on the Brain:

The Self and Its Brain: Popper and Eccles

The Brain User's Manual: Diagram Group (Berkely Publishing Corporation, 1982)

Current Research into Specific Learning Difficulties: Neurological Aspects (Berkshire and Oxfordshire Dyslexia Associations, 1982)

Nutrition and Health:

Natural Healing: Michio Kushi (East West Publications, 1978)

Biological Transmutations: Kervran/Abehsera (Swan Publishing Co., 1972)

Nutrition Almanac: John D. Kirschmann (McGraw-Hill Book Co., 1984)

Medical Applications of Clinical Nutrition: Ed. Jeffrey Bland (Keats Publishing, 1982)

Healing Hypoglycaemia: Ana Best

Nutritional Influences on Illness: Melvyn R. Werbach (Thorsons, 1987)

Food Chemical Sensitivity: Robert Buist (Prism Press, 1986)

Food Intolerance: What It is and How to Cope With It: Robert Buist (Harper and Row, 1984)

The Allergy Self-Help Book: Sharon Faelten (Pan Books, 1983)

Nutritional Medicine: Dr Stephen Davies and Dr Alan Stewart

Better Health through Natural Healing: Ross Tratler (Thorsons, 1987)

Candida Albicans: Leon Chaitow (Thorsons, 1987)

Evening Primrose Oil: Judy Graham (Thorsons, 1984)

Handbook of Herbal Health: Kitty Campion (Sphere Books Ltd, 1985)

The Herb User's Guide: David Hoffman (Thorsons, 1987)

A Modern Herbal: M. Grieve (Dover Publications)

Complementary Medicine:

Oriental Diagnosis: Michio Kushi (Sunwheel Publications, 1976)
Touch For Health: John F. Thie (DeVorss & Co., 1973)
Acupressure Way of Health: Jin Shin Do: Iona Teeguarden (Japan Publications, 1978, 1981)
Do-It-Yourself Shiatsu: Wataru Ohashi (Unwin Paperbacks, 1976)
Advanced G-Jo/The Natural Healer's Acupressure Handbook Vol 2: Michael Blate (Routledge, 1983)
Stories the Feet Have Told: Eunice Ingham (Rochester, N.Y., 1959)
Hand Reflexology: Key to Perfect Health: Mildred Carter (Parker Publishing Co., Inc., 1975)
Awareness through Movement: Moshe Feldenkrais (Penguin, 1984)
Health-Building: Dr Randolph Stone (1980)
Prenatal Therapy and the Retarded Child: Robert St. John

Medical Reference:

A Modern Course in Biology: Dearden and Dearden (Pergamon Press, 1969)
Faber's Anatomical Atlas: Maxwell, Burdon and Macdonald (Faber and Faber, 1962)
Anatomy and Physiology for Nurses: Armstrong and Jackson (Bailliere Tindall, 1972)
Black's Medical Dictionary: William Thomson (Black, 1971)
The Chemicals of Life: Isaac Asimov (New American Library, 1954)